THE SKY
OBSERVER'S
GUIDE

CEPHEUS

URSA MINOR

DRACO

Deneb

CYGNUS

Vega

CORONA BOREALIS

BOÖTES

LYRA

HERCULES

PEGASUS

Arcturus

DELPHINUS

AQUILA

Altair

AQUARIUS

OPHIUCHUS

VIRGO

CAPRICORNUS

LIBRA

Fomalhaut

Antares

HYD

SAGITTARIUS

SCORPIUS

GRUS

LUPUS

CEN

INDUS

ARA

Rigil Kentaurus

TUCANA

Hadar

TRIANGULUM AUSTRALE

0h   22h   20h   18h   16h   14h

+90°

+60°

+30°

±0°

-30°

-60°

-90°

0h   22h   20h   18h   16h   14h

C395395

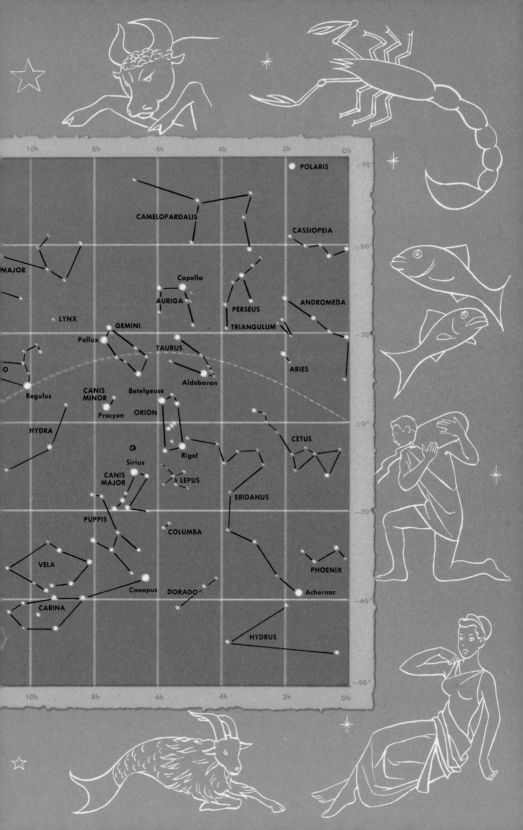

THE SKY OBSERVER'S GUIDE

A Handbook for Amateur Astronomers
BY NEWTON MAYALL, MARGARET MAYALL
AND JEROME WYCKOFF

PAINTINGS AND DIAGRAMS
BY JOHN POLGREEN

GOLDEN PRESS · NEW YORK

CONTENTS

Third Printing, 1964

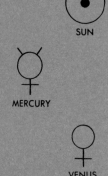
SUN

MERCURY

VENUS

EARTH

MOON

MARS

SATURN

JUPITER

URANUS

NEPTUNE

PLUTO

BECOMING A SKY OBSERVER

All of us, from childhood, have gazed at the sky in wonder. Sun and moon, the wandering planets, the fiery trails of comets and meteors— these are things to marvel at. Man will never tire of looking up into the tremendous, sparkling bowl of space.

Skywatching was undoubtedly a pastime of prehistoric man. The ancient Egyptians and Babylonians, several thousand years ago, observed the heavens carefully enough to devise quite accurate calendars. Observations by Copernicus, Galileo, and others in the sixteenth and seventeenth centuries were among the first great steps to modern science. Even today, although it is often a matter of complicated figures and formulas, the science of astronomy depends on observation.

Astronomy for Everybody

Astronomy is for the amateur as well as the professional. The amateur can see for himself the sights that stirred Galileo, the Herschels, and other great astronomers. A high-school boy may be the first to see a comet, a rug salesman may discover a nova, and a housewife can help in detecting the re-entry of a rocket or artificial satellite. An amateur's faithful observations of a variable star may be just the data that a big observatory needs.

Mars in color: This photo of the red planet, always a favorite, is one of the finest ever made. Printed page cannot fully convey delicate hues of original.

teur astronomy is greatest and most long-lasting when they are working on observation programs that are scientifically useful.

Observing with Unaided Eyes

Even an observer without binoculars or a telescope can see many wonders of the heavens. The important thing is to know how to look and what to look for. The constellations can be traced and identified. Some star clusters can be located, and eclipses and some comets observed. The changing positions of Sun, Moon, and the brighter planets can be closely watched, and some artificial satellites can be seen. Meteors can be noticed; the brightness and length of their trails can be estimated. It is, in fact, a good idea to get used to finding your way about the sky with the eyes alone before trying a telescope.

Binoculars and Telescope

Your first look at the heavens through good binoculars can be exciting. Binoculars gather 20 to 40 times as much light as the human eye. They bring into view such dramatic features as mountains and craters of the Moon, sunspots, the four larger satellites of Jupiter, double stars and star clusters, and luminous clouds of cosmic gas such as the famous nebula in Orion. (Before observing Sun, see page 49!)

Although in some regions weather and climate are often unfavorable, any interested person in any part of the world can become a sky observer. The aspect of the sky differs from place to place, but the majesty of Sun and Moon, of stars and planets and nebulas, is to be seen everywhere.

This book is a guide to observing —to the use of binoculars and telescopes, the locating of sky objects, what objects to look for and how best to see them. The beginning observer should have also a book on general astronomy. Even a little knowledge greatly increases the pleasure of observing, and it prepares us to undertake real astronomical projects. Most old hands at observing have found, in fact, that the fun of amateur

With no more than binoculars, some observers do useful scientific work, such as recording light changes in variable stars and watching for novas and comets.

A telescope is obtained by every serious amateur sooner or later. Refractors, with lenses 1½ to 4 inches in diameter, and reflectors, with mirrors 3 to 6 inches in diameter, are popular types.

The light-gathering and magnifying power of telescopes brings out details of the Moon's surface. It reveals Jupiter's larger satellites and its banded clouds, as well as markings on Mars and the rings of Saturn.

With telescopes we can "split" double stars and distinguish star clusters, nebulas, comets, and sunspots. We can watch the Moon occult (that is, pass in front of) stars and planets. Light fluctuations of dim variable stars and novas can be detected.

Small telescopes have their limitations, yet good ones can give surprising performance. For example, when conditions are right, an observer with a good 3-inch refractor or 6-inch reflector can see some features of Jupiter and Saturn more distinctly than they appear in photographs taken with giant observatory telescopes.

Great Nebula in Orion: Famous nebula is painted as seen by artist in 8-inch telescope at 200 power. Pattern of four stars near center is "Trapezium." Compare with sketch, page 93, and photo, page 95.

Fun with the Camera

Many amateurs, however, do make use of the special advantages of the camera. The eye can "hold" only the light it is receiving in the present instant, but photographic film can "store up" light over a long period of exposure. Thus an amateur's camera can detect faint objects which the eye, even with the aid of the Palomar telescope, could never see. Even with a simple, inexpensive camera, exciting and useful results are possible.

Homemade Telescopes

Some amateurs, not content with factory-made telescopes, have made their own. They grind the lenses and mirrors, and design the mountings. It takes special knowledge and skill, yet hundreds of amateurs have made instruments that perform splendidly.

Telescope-making classes are held at some planetariums, universities, and observatories. Books on telescope making are available from booksellers.

Organizations of Amateurs

Many amateur observers belong to national organizations. These give members information on equipment, observing techniques, and standard methods of reporting their work. They set up observing programs and receive observational data from members. Data are sent to observatories for use in programs of research. Some organizations publish news of developments that interest amateurs.

Numerous groups have been organized locally. They observe together, compare equipment, and promote public interest in astronomy.

Clarence P. Custer, M.D.

Serious amateur: Some amateurs have developed elaborate equipment capable of high performance. This 12-inch reflector has Springfield mounting.

Six-inch Reflector

Three-inch Refractor

Satellite-tracking Telescope

Three types of telescope: Reflector, using mirror for objective, is common all-purpose design. Refractor, with lens for objective, also is all-purpose. Tracking telescope is small instrument with extra-wide field.

THE OBSERVER'S EQUIPMENT

Charts and Books

Just as we gather a supply of maps and booklets before touring the country, so we must gather certain sources of information before touring the sky.

This book provides all necessary information for a good start in sky observing. The index will guide you to explanations of observing techniques and equipment, to lists of interesting objects to look for, and to tables indicating where and when to look for planets, eclipses, meteor showers, and periodic comets. For more background in astronomy, the reader may turn to books and periodicals recommended on page 113.

Hundreds of stars, nebulas, and other objects can be located with the aid of the maps on pages 114-123. For fainter objects the more detailed charts to be found in a star atlas become indispensable. There are atlases of convenient size that show nearly all stars as faint as can be seen with binoculars. For serious work with a telescope, still more detailed charts are needed.

Some beginners use a planisphere to learn constellations. One type has a "wheel" on which is printed a map of the constellations. The wheel is rotated within an envelope that has a window. When the wheel is set for any particular month, day, and hour, the window shows the positions of the constellations at that time.

For star-watching: Popular binocular designs come in leather case, with caps to protect lenses.

Binocular Facts

Every observer should own a good pair of binoculars. These gather far more light than the eye, magnify images, and use the capacity of both eyes.

Opera-glass binoculars consist essentially of two small refracting telescopes mounted together. At the front of each is a large lens, the objective, which gathers the light. At the rear is a smaller lens, the eyepiece or ocu-

lar, which does the magnifying. In the front part of the eyepiece is a third element, the erecting lens, which is necessary to prevent our getting an upside-down view.

In the large prism binoculars, the objectives are centered farther apart. The light rays from them must be brought closer together before they reach the eyepieces. This is done by a pair of prisms in each tube.

Opera glasses have objectives of about an inch in diameter and a magnifying power of 2 to 3. Prism binoculars, with their larger objectives and higher magnification, are preferable for astronomical observing. Popular types have objectives of 35 to 50 millimeters (about 1⅜ to 2 inches), and magnify 6 to 10 times.

Binoculars labeled "7x50" magnify 7 times and have an objective 50 millimeters in diameter. The area of the objective determines light-gathering ability; so 7x50 binoculars gather more light than 7x35's.

Binoculars vary also as to field of view. The field is the whole circular area we see through the instrument. Thus in binoculars with a 6° field we see an area of sky 6° in diameter—equivalent to an area 100 feet in diameter at 1,000 feet.

Heavy binoculars make the arms tired and unsteady. Generally, 7-power binoculars are about the

Magnification: Photos illustrate Moon as seen with unaided eye and through 7-power binoculars.

limit for convenient handling. Bigger binoculars ordinarily must be used with some support.

Telescope Principles

Astronomical telescopes are of two main types: refracting and reflecting.

In a simple refractor, light is gathered by a lens, and magnification is done by the eyepiece. There is no erecting lens, because this would cut down the amount of light delivered to the eye. The image seen by the observer is inverted, but this makes no difference in observation of stars.

With the telescope the observer usually gets several removable eye-pieces. These are used for different degrees of magnification, as desired.

Every good astronomical telescope has a finder. This is a small telescope, usually of 5 or 6 power, with a wide field, mounted on the main tube. It is used for aiming the telescope, because the field seen through a high-power telescope is very small.

Astronomical refractors generally have a star diagonal, also. It bends the light at right angles before it reaches the eyepiece, and this allows us to observe objects overhead with comfort.

Reflecting telescopes use a mirror, not a lens, for the objective. Light from the star falls upon the mirror and is reflected to a diagonal mirror

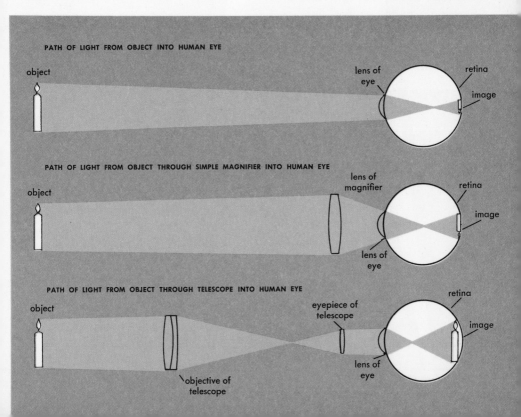

or prism in the tube. This in turn reflects the light to the eyepiece.

The mirror used in a reflector is a highly polished concave glass disk coated usually with aluminum or silver.

Amateur astronomers like to argue about the merits of refractors and reflectors. Mostly, they agree that a refractor gets out of adjustment less easily than a reflector. Less maintenance, such as realignment or the resurfacing of mirrors, is necessary. But reflectors are generally less expensive and are more readily made by amateurs.

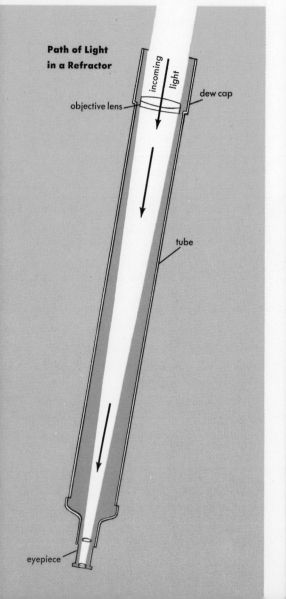

Path of Light in a Refractor

incoming light

objective lens

dew cap

tube

eyepiece

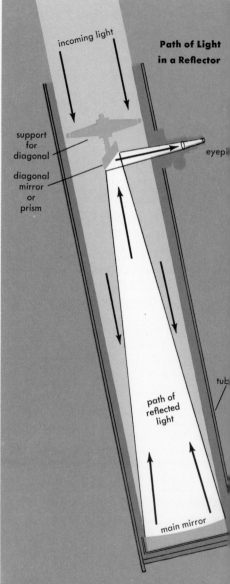

incoming light

Path of Light in a Reflector

support for diagonal

diagonal mirror or prism

eyepi

path of reflected light

tub

main mirror

Light-gathering power: Comparison of 6-inch mirror, 50mm. binocular lens, and human eye.

Light-gathering Power

The telescope's ability to reveal faint objects depends mainly upon the size of its objective. A lens 3 inches in diameter will gather two times as much light as a 2-inch lens, and a 6-inch will gather four times as much light as a 3-inch.

The table below shows how our ability to see faint objects depends upon the size of the objective used. The fainter the object, the larger is the objective required for seeing it. These figures are only approximate. Actual performance depends partly upon seeing conditions, quality of the instrument, and the observer's vision.

How Size of Objective Determines Visibility of Objects

Diameter of Objective (inches)	Faintest Magnitude* Visible	Number of Stars Visible
1	9.0	117,000
1¾	10.0	324,000
2¾	11.0	870,000
4½	12.0	2,270,000
7	13.0	5,700,000
11	14.0	13,800,000
17½	15.0	32,000,000

*See page 22 for explanation of magnitude.

Magnifying Power

The eyepiece of a telescope bends the light rays so that they form a larger image on the retina of the eye than would be formed if no eyepiece were used. The image size depends upon the focal length of the eyepiece. The focal length is the distance between the eyepiece and the point at which the converging rays of light meet. The shorter the focal length, the larger the image. Focal lengths of typical telescopic eyepieces range from ¼ inch to 1½ or 2 inches.

Magnification given by a telescope depends not only upon the eyepiece being used, but also upon the focal length of the objective. The longer the focal length of the objective, the greater the magnification obtained with any given eyepiece.

To determine the magnification being obtained, we divide the focal length of the eyepiece into the focal length of the objective. For example, if the focal length of the objective is 50 inches, a ½-inch eyepiece will give 100 power ("100x").

15

Limits of Magnification

Theoretically, there is no limit to the magnifying power of an instrument. Practically, there is. As we use eyepieces of higher power, the image becomes more and more fuzzy, though larger. Finally the fuzziness becomes so extreme that the object is seen less distinctly than at a lower power.

The practical magnifying limit depends mainly upon the diameter of the objective. For well-made telescopes the limit is about 50 times the diameter of the objective, in inches. This means about 150x for a 3-inch telescope, or 300x for a 6-inch. As the observer becomes familiar with his own telescope, he may find it has a somewhat different limit—say, 40 or 60. The exact figure will depend partly upon the atmospheric conditions.

Resolving Power

The resolving power of an instrument is its ability to show fine detail—for example, markings on planets. To determine the theoretical resolving power of an objective, divide the number 4.5 by the diameter of the objective in inches. The answer (known as "Dawes' limit") is the distance, in seconds of arc, between the closest objects that can be distinguished.

A good 3-inch lens should separate objects about 1.5 seconds apart. One second of arc is 1/60th of a minute or 1/3600th of a degree. A degree is 1/90th of the distance from the horizon to the zenith (point in the sky directly overhead). The average unaided human eye, under good conditions, can distinguish stars about 180 seconds apart.

The performance of an objective depends upon quality of the glass, optical surfaces, seeing conditions, and alignment of the telescope.

Telescope Mountings

Since it gives such high magnification, a telescope must have a strong, steady mounting. The two main types of mountings are the alt-azimuth and the equatorial.

The alt-azimuth mounting is the simpler. It allows two motions of the telescope — up and down, an "altitude" motion; and horizontal, an "azimuth" motion. This is a good general-purpose mounting. It is light, portable, and easily taken down and set up; usually it rests on a tripod. Most telescopes with objectives of less than 3 inches have this type of mounting.

Magnification: Excessive magnification of image spoils it. Inset shows proper magnification.

The equatorial mounting is designed to be set up in a certain way in a specially prepared location, though it too is used for some small portable telescopes. In its simplest form, the equatorial has two axes at right angles to each other. It is an all-purpose mounting, generally used for serious work. To make the most of it, we must set it up properly (pages 28-29).

Some equatorials have setting circles. These make it possible to aim the instrument automatically at the right point in the heavens (pages 38-39).

Besides the basic equipment that usually comes with a telescope, an observer can obtain useful extra equipment, some of which is described on pages 106-108.

Quality of Equipment

Both for serious astronomical work and for plain fun, quality in equipment is all-important.

Test binoculars or a telescope before buying. Haziness, milkiness, or rainbow colors in the field are a sign of poor optical parts. Good instruments will reduce stars to neat points of light, and show distant print without distortion. If an object being viewed "dances" when the telescope is lightly touched, the mounting is below par.

Price is not always an indicator of quality. Some low-cost instruments

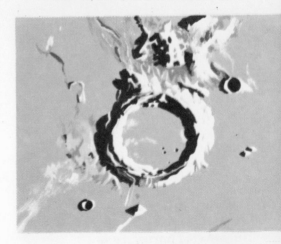

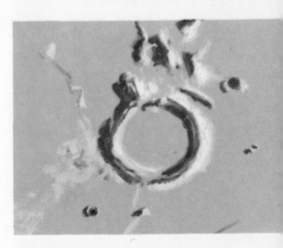

Resolution: Moon crater Archimedes well resolved (above) and poorly resolved (below).

turn out well, but there is always risk in buying them. If possible, the buyer should have the advice of an expert.

Some buyers exaggerate the importance of "power." They buy the most powerful telescope available at a given price—only to learn, later, that a smaller instrument of better quality would have given greater satisfaction.

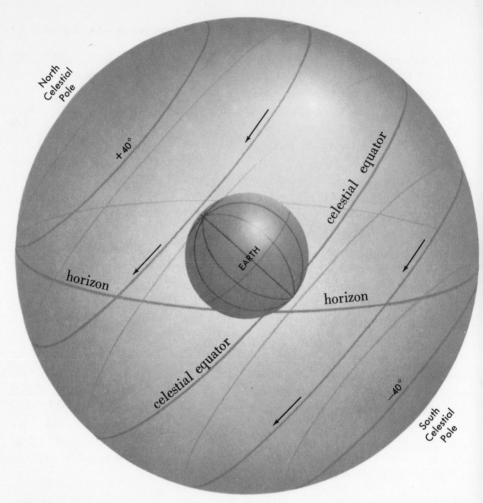

Celestial sphere: For observers at latitude of New York (41°N.), stars within 41° of north celestial pole never go below horizon, and stars within 41° of south celestial pole never rise above horizon. Earth rotates from west to east within celestial sphere. (Diagram represents sphere as seen from outside.)

UNDERSTANDING THE SKY

A yardful of expensive equipment cannot make up for an ignorance of astronomy. Every observer should have a basic astronomy guide and read it. But here is a short review of facts that directly affect observing.

Astronomers call the sky, as seen from Earth, the "celestial sphere." It can be imagined as an enormous hollow ball with Earth at the center, and with the stars "painted" around the inside surface. As Earth rotates, the stars seem to parade by.

Exactly what section of sky the observer can see depends partly upon his location. The sky seen from the North Pole is completely different from the sky seen from the South Pole. Between the poles there is an overlapping. An observer looking south from New York sees a portion of the northern part of the sky that is seen from Rio de Janeiro. People in Rio can see only the southern part of the sky area seen from New York. Theoretically, a person at the Equator can see the whole sky, but he can see only half of it at once.

At night the sky appears to pass steadily overhead, east to west. This seeming motion is due to Earth's rotation. From the North Pole, the sky appears to turn like an enormous wheel, counterclockwise, with its hub directly overhead at the so-called North Star. From the South Pole the sky appears as a wheel turning clockwise.

For an observer halfway between the Equator and the North or South Pole, the hub is just halfway up— 45° from the horizon. Stars within 45° of the hub remain in view all night as they move around it. Objects farther than 45° from the hub rise and set.

Objects near the center of the wheel seem to move slower than stars farther out. All, however, are moving at the same speed in terms of degrees. Each object has about 360° to cover in 24 hours.

The Stars by Seasons

Stars and planets appear to move at a speed of about 15° per hour, covering about 360° in 24 hours. But each evening, a star or planet rises about 4 minutes earlier than the evening before. This daily gain is due to the progress of Earth in its journey

Big Dipper as seen from different latitudes: Paintings show altitude of constellation as seen from central Canada (left) and from Long Island (right) at same time. Big Dipper appears to revolve counterclockwise.

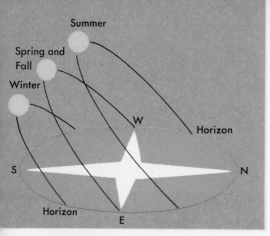

The Sun's changing path: Path is low in winter, higher in spring and fall, highest in summer. Diagram is for northern hemisphere. For southern hemisphere compass points would be reversed.

around the Sun, and amounts to a gain of a day in the course of a year.

Stars that rise and set at any particular latitude, therefore, are not visible all year. During some of the year, the time between rising and setting will occur during daylight.

The star charts on pages 114-123 will show that each constellation, at a given hour, is farther west in summer than in spring, farther west in fall than in summer, and so on.

"Fixed" Stars—Moving Planets

Stars are so far away that, though traveling many miles per second, they seem motionless. Constellations remain the same year after year. Only over hundreds of years could changes in constellation shapes be noticed by the unaided eye.

But all objects within our solar system are much closer. As seen from Earth, they move against the background of the constellations. The Moon, during most of the year, rises an average of 50 minutes later each night, and the height of its path in the heavens changes with the seasons. Positions of all the planets, asteroids, and comets change as well. The Sun's motion against the background of stars is not noticeable, but does occur.

The Ecliptic and the Zodiac

The path of the Sun against the background of stars is called the eclip-

Why constellations change with seasons: As Earth revolves around Sun, the part of the sky that we see at night changes accordingly. In a year the full parade of constellations is completed.

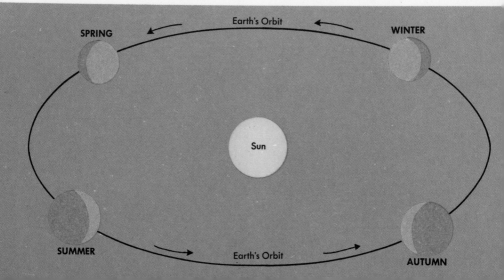

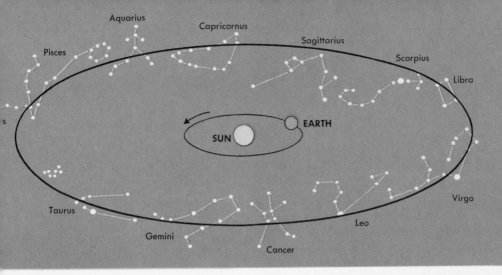

Constellations of Zodiac: Band of constellations is drawn as if seen from outside, with constellations in foreground reversed. Sun is "in" a constellation when between that constellation and Earth.

tic. In the course of each day, the Sun moves about 1° against the background. In a year it makes the full circuit of 360°.

As Earth circles the Sun, its axis stays tilted at about 23½°. Hence the position of the ecliptic in the sky appears to change as the year progresses. The ecliptic is directly overhead at 23½° north latitude on about June 21, and overhead at 23½° south latitude on about December 22. On these dates, called the "solstices," Earth is at opposite points of its orbit.

All the planets, and the Moon also, follow pathways that remain within about 8° of the ecliptic. That is, they follow an avenue about 16° wide, with the ecliptic in the middle. To this avenue the ancients gave the name Zodiac. Its twelve divisions are called "signs of the Zodiac."

Asteroid's trail: In time-exposure photo, clock drive compensated for Earth's rotation and thus kept camera aimed at this star field. Asteroid, moving against background of stars, made trail.

Yerkes Obs.

Ordinarily we describe the locations of planets with reference to Zodiac constellations. Thus, when we say, "Jupiter is in Pisces," we mean that at the present time Jupiter is in the area of sky outlined by Pisces.

Signs of the Zodiac

♈	Aries	♎	Libra
♉	Taurus	♏	Scorpius
♊	Gemini	♐	Sagittarius
♋	Cancer	♑	Capricornus
♌	Leo	♒	Aquarius
♍	Virgo	♓	Pisces

Magnitudes

The magnitude of a celestial body is its brightness, compared to the brightness of other celestial objects, as seen from Earth. This brightness depends not only upon the amount of light the object emits, but also upon its distance from Earth.

Some stars vary in magnitude because their light output changes. Planets and comets vary in magnitude as they move nearer to the Earth or farther away.

Magnitude 1 is 2½ times the brightness of magnitude 2; magnitude 2 is 2½ times magnitude 3; magnitude 3 is 2½ times magnitude 4; and so forth. Thus, a star of magnitude 1 is 6.3 times as bright as a star of magnitude 3, and 16 times as bright as a star of magnitude 4.

Some objects are of "minus" magnitudes. Thus, the Sun is of magnitude −27, and the full Moon −13.

For convenience, magnitudes are sometimes rounded off:

Magnitudes from	to	Are Considered as Magnitude
−1.5	−0.6	−1.0
−0.5	+0.4	0.0
+0.5	+1.4	+1.0
+1.5	+2.4	+2.0
+2.5	+3.4	+3.0
+3.5	+4.4	+4.0

and so forth.

On a clear, dark night, the unaided eye may detect stars as faint as magnitude 5 or 6. Binoculars help us to see "down" to magnitude 8 or 9, and a 6-inch telescope to about 13.

The brightness of planets changes according to their positions with respect to Sun and Earth. Planets outside Earth's orbit are brightest when Earth is between them and the Sun. The magnitude of Mars, for example, varies from −2.8 to +1.6, and Jupiter from −2.5 to −1.4.

Planets shine more steadily than do stars. Light from a star reaches us as if from a tiny point, and atmospheric interference with this thin stream of light is quite noticeable. Light from a planet comes as if from a disk; the stream is thicker and the atmosphere has less apparent effect upon it.

Magnitudes: Approximate magnitudes of many stars can be estimated by comparison with stars in Little Dipper and vicinity of Southern Cross.

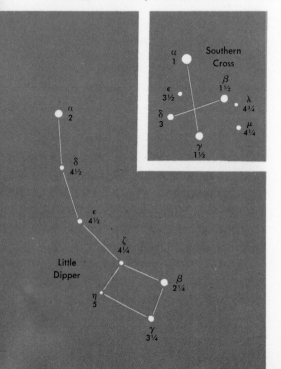

Mt. Wilson and Palomar Obs.
Cluster of diamonds: Pleiades, an open cluster of six stars to unaided eyes, becomes glittering spray in binoculars. Telescopes of 6 inches and more reveal faint clouds of glowing gas, as in this photo.

FIRST STEPS IN OBSERVING

Local conditions always put a limit on what an observer can see. Faint stars and other dim objects become lost in the glow of city lights. Heavy traffic on a nearby street may cause a star image in one's telescope to shiver and shake. If the telescope is pointed at a planet that appears just over a neighbor's roof, heated air rising from the roof may turn the planet's image into a distorted, "boiling" blob. Gusts of wind, clouds suddenly rolling in, heavy dew, and inconveniently located trees are other hazards.

The observer with a broad, open horizon, free from interfering lights, is lucky. City observers sometimes must retreat to a park or a suburb to see more than the Moon or a few bright stars. The suburbanite often must place his telescope so that a building or hedge will block the light from a neighbor's living room or front porch.

Comfort and Seeing Conditions

Unnecessary discomforts can quickly spoil the fun of observing. In winter, warm clothing is vital. In summer, a mosquito repellent may be necessary. In any season, a stool

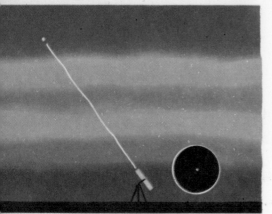

"Seeing": Turbulence of atmosphere (upper picture) usually means poor seeing, as indicated by large, "boiling" star image (inset). Quieter atmosphere (below) allows better seeing.

or chair will spell comfort during long periods at the telescope. For observers using binoculars, a reclining chair makes it easier to observe objects high overhead.

The scattered, puffy cumulus clouds of a fair day usually vanish soon after sunset. But stratus and cirrus clouds, often associated with rainy weather, are more likely to linger.

Oddly enough, the clearest night is not always the best for observing. The atmosphere may be quite turbu-

lent. Differences in density between warm and cold air currents cause light to be refracted, or bent, irregularly as it comes down through the atmosphere. The images we see in the telescope may then, as astronomers say, "boil." A slightly hazy sky, with relatively still air, is preferred.

The nearer a celestial object is to the horizon, the more poorly it will be seen, usually. Its light comes slanting through Earth's atmosphere and thus passes through more disturbing air currents and dust than does light from an object higher in the heavens.

Moonlight, too, is a hazard. As the Moon waxes, stars and planets fade. By the time the Moon is full, little else can be seen.

Using Our Eyes

As we leave a lighted house, our eyes begin adapting to the darkness. After a few minutes we can detect objects several times dimmer than at first. Thereafter, our ability to see in the dark improves slowly for hours.

To keep this sensitivity, we avoid looking at bright objects. Any light used during observation, such as for consulting star charts, should be dim, and it should be red. (Red impairs sensitivity of the eye to light less than other colors.) A small red Christmas-tree light on an extension cord, or a flashlight covered with red cloth or cellophane, will do.

To detect faint objects, experienced observers often use "averted" vision. They look a little to one side of the object, so that its light will fall on a more sensitive part of the retina of the eye.

Finding Celestial Objects

Constellations are the observer's signposts. So every observer should know the principal constellations visible at his latitude.

The charts on pages 114-123 show all the constellations and the time of the year when each is conveniently located for seeing. Constellations can be learned by using either these charts or a planisphere (page 11).

Once the constellations have been learned, it is easy to locate the brighter stars and planets. First we find the constellation in which the object is known to appear. Then we narrow the hunt down to the right part of the constellation.

Suppose you want to find the great red star Betelgeuse. You look it up in the index, which refers to the chart on page 116. There you see that Betelgeuse is at the northeast corner of a group of bright stars forming the constellation Orion. The chart shows the position of Orion in relation to the other constellations, and the time of year when it is conveniently visible. With this information, you find Orion in the sky rather easily (if the time of year and time of night are

John Polgreen

Signpost: Constellations are guides to faint celestial objects. This time-exposure photo of Orion vicinity reveals more stars than are seen by unaided eyes (compare with map, page 116).

right), and you identify Betelgeuse.

Betelgeuse is easy to spot because it is red and prominent. Most sky objects are fainter and tend to become lost in the multitude of stars visible in binoculars and telescopes. To find a faint object, we must first identify bright stars near it and then use these as guides. Their positions are easier to hold in mind if we notice the patterns they form—such as squares, triangles, circles, and loops.

Suppose now that you want to get a look at the famous star cluster M13 in the constellation Hercules. The

25

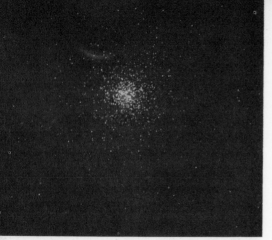

M13: Cluster, faint to unaided eye, is hard to find unless one knows just where to look. Photo suggests appearance in small telescope.

chart (page 121) shows that it is located on an almost straight line between two stars forming the west side of a "keystone" at the center of the constellation. You find the constellation and the keystone. With reference to the North Star, you decide which is the west side of the keystone. Then, with the help of binoculars (because the object is very faint to the eye), the cluster M13 is spotted.

Estimating Sky Distances

Observers soon get accustomed to measuring sky distances in "degrees." The distance from the zenith (point in the sky exactly overhead) to the horizon is 90°; so half this distance is 45°, and so on. By this standard the distance between the two brightest stars in the bowl of the Big Dipper—

Sky clock: Diagram shows apparent movement of Big Dipper around north celestial pole. Revolution is completed in about 23 hours 56 minutes. Motion is counterclockwise.

the "Pointers"—is about 5°. In the southern sky, the distance between the two stars forming the leg of the Southern Cross (Crux) is about 5° also. With such known distances in mind, one can more easily estimate distances elsewhere in the sky.

Binoculars, too, make a good yardstick. In binoculars with a 7° field, for instance, the diameter of the circle of sky shown is always 7°. We can measure long distances across the sky by 7° steps.

In a telescope, the size of the field varies according to the power of the eyepiece being used. The field may be something like $\frac{1}{2}$° with the $\frac{3}{4}$-inch eyepiece, or 1° with the $1\frac{1}{4}$-inch.

The field obtained with each eyepiece can be determined by observation. Point the telescope toward an easily seen group of stars near the equator. Look through the eyepiece and note the stars at opposite sides of the field; then check your atlas to determine the distance between these

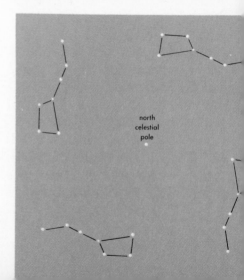

north
celestial
pole

Holding a star chart: Chart is held so that star patterns correspond to their positions in sky.

stars. The distance is your field of view in degrees.

The eyepiece field can be determined also by noting how long it takes a star near the equator to cross the field. The motion is $\frac{1}{4}°$ per minute.

Getting Sky Directions Right

To avoid confusion as to sky directions, these must be thought of with respect to the celestial pole. In the northern hemisphere we think of the North Star, which is only about 1° from the true pole.

Suppose you have found Betelgeuse in Orion and want to find μ Orionis, a dimmer star in the same constellation. A star atlas shows that μ Orionis is about 2° north and 1° east of Betelgeuse. Looking at Betelgeuse again, you mentally draw from it a line to the North Star. This line is in the direction of north. At right

angles to north, and in the direction from which the stars are moving, is east. With your mental yardstick or with binoculars, you measure 2° north and 1° east from Betelgeuse, and there is μ Orionis.

Directions are most easily confused near the celestial pole. Remember: the motion of the stars, in the northern hemisphere, as they revolve around the pole, is counterclockwise; that is, westward for the stars above the pole, and eastward for the stars below the pole. In the southern hemisphere the stars revolve in a clockwise motion around the pole; that is, eastward for those stars above the pole, and westward for those below the pole.

When using a chart, hold it up toward the sky in the direction in which you are looking. Rotate it until the star patterns on the map correspond to their positions in the sky.

27

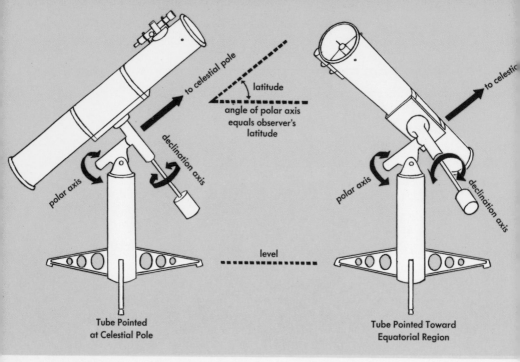

to celestial pole

latitude

angle of polar axis
equals observer's
latitude

declination axis

polar axis

to celestic

declination axis

polar axis

level

**Tube Pointed
at Celestial Pole**

**Tube Pointed Toward
Equatorial Region**

Orientation of an equatorial telescope: Proper placement makes telescope easier to use.

USING A TELESCOPE

Our first look through a telescope at the Moon or a sparkling star cluster can be exciting indeed. But in the long run, the fun of sky observing depends upon our increasing skill with the telescope. Even a small instrument, if it is a good one properly used, can perform superbly and give tremendous satisfaction.

Telescopes are ordinarily kept dismantled. The ends of the tube are usually covered with dustproof bags or caps. The eyepieces are kept in a convenient dustproof box.

Getting a simple alt-azimuth telescope ready for use is usually just a matter of setting up the tripod or base and attaching the tube to it. The location should be level, and where neighborhood lights, trees, and buildings will not interfere (see page 23). If the telescope is put on a platform or table, this must be firm. The legs of a tripod must be securely set to prevent sliding or vibration.

With an equatorial telescope, set up the tripod or base first, then attach the counterweight, and finally fasten the tube in the cradle. In dismantling, the tube is removed first, then the counterweight. For safety, a heavy telescope should be disassembled before being moved from place to place.

Orienting an Equatorial

Both alt-azimuth and equatorial telescopes can be set up and used in any position. But the equatorial telescope will work better if the polar axis points approximately to the celestial pole. For best results, the telescope should be set up in this way:

Place the pedestal or tripod legs on the ground so that the polar axis points directly at the celestial pole. (In the northern hemisphere, the pole is about at the location of the North Star; see chart, page 114.) Clamp the declination axis to prevent motion on that axis. Then, to check the alignment, look through the finder as you move the tube back and forth on the polar axis. If the pole remains near the center of the field in the finder, the alignment is good. If the alignment is poor, it can be improved by slight readjustments of pedestal or legs.

The alignment may be considered good enough when the pole stays within a degree of the center of the field in the finder while the tube is moved on the polar axis. The pavement or ground should then be marked in some way so that the pedestal or legs can be set up with less fuss next time.

Motions of the Equatorial

Properly placed, the equatorial is remarkably easy to use. With both axes unclamped, there is free motion in any direction. With the polar axis clamped, there is north-and-south motion only. This is convenient for scanning the sky as the Earth rotates. Or, with the declination axis clamped, there is east-and-west motion only. Thus we can keep the telescope trained on an object for a long time simply by moving the tube around the polar axis to compensate for Earth's rotation. Some telescopes are equipped with a clock drive (page 106) to provide this motion.

Selecting the Eyepiece

Most telescopes come with three eyepieces for sky observing. An additional one may be included for terrestrial observing, because celestial eyepieces invert the image. The terrestrial eyepiece is not used for sky observing, because the additional

Alt-azimuth mounting: Lacking advantages of equatorial, alt-azimuth mounting is nevertheless sound and useful. Observer is using star diagonal.

lenses required to make the image upright reduce the amount of light received by the eye.

In the eyepiece holder is an adapter—a metal tube. The eyepiece is inserted in the adapter, then moved back and forth until you find the position that gives the best image.

With a refractor, the star diagonal is used for observing objects high in the sky. Insert one end into the adapter; into the other end goes the eyepiece. In some refractors the diagonal must be used at all times in order to get the eyepiece far enough from the objective.

Beginners tend to use their most powerful eyepiece too much. Seasoned observers know that magnification is not all-important. They choose the eyepiece that will do the particular job best.

If a wide field of view is needed, use a low-power eyepiece. Low power is preferred when "sweeping" large areas of sky (as for comets or novas), when looking at wide star clusters such as the Pleiades, or when we want to see the whole Moon in the field rather than just part of it. Low power is best also when we are hunting for an unfamiliar faint object; a more powerful eyepiece can be substituted after we have found it.

A higher-power eyepiece is needed for splitting close double stars, seeing fine detail on Moon and Planets, and detecting individual stars in close-packed clusters. High power also tends to darken the sky background and thus helps us to detect very dim objects. However, as we use higher and higher power on any object, its details lose sharpness and clarity.

Eyepieces, magnification, and field: Moon crater as seen in small telescope with eyepieces giving low, medium, and high power. Field diminishes as magnification increases. Sharpness of detail also lessens.

Lick 0

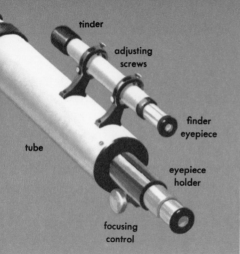

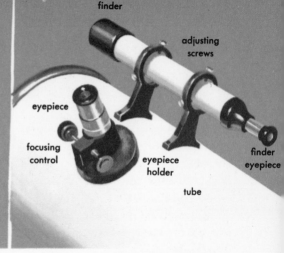

Finder and Eyepiece on a Refractor **Finder and Eyepiece on a Reflector**

Special eyepieces have been designed for safe direct observation of the sun. See pages 49-50.

An accessory that many sky observers have found very satisfying is the so-called Barlow lens. This is used in combination with any eyepiece to increase magnification. At the same time it cuts down the field of view.

The observer should learn the field of view of his telescope given by each of his eyepieces. An easy method is described on page 27.

Experience teaches that the observing conditions each evening put certain limits on the performance of our telescope. The faintest magnitudes that we can detect vary from night to night. At one time we may be able to use 350x on an object before it "comes apart," and at another time the limit may be 200x. Some evenings we may be able to "split" the double star Castor with 125x, and at other times the seeing may be so poor that 250x will not do it.

Sighting the Telescope

Sighting an astronomical telescope by just pointing the tube is usually not accurate enough. Ordinarily we need to use the finder. This is likely to have a field (inverted) of 5 or 6°. If the finder has been exactly lined up with the tube, an object centered in the finder will be found centered in the eyepiece, too.

Sighting bright planets and other prominent objects with the finder is easy. But for faint objects the step method may be necessary. Consulting our chart, we note the object's position with respect to the nearest bright stars. Using these as signposts, we work our way to the object sought.

As the tube of a reflecting telescope is moved, it may have to be rotated on its longitudinal axis in order to keep the eyepiece and finder in a position comfortable for viewing. In all good reflectors a rotatable tube is standard. In the refractor, a diagonal

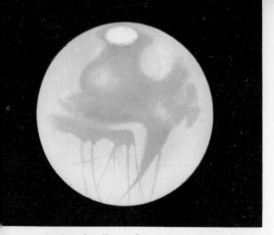

Seeing detail on planet: This painting, seen in normal light at distance of 40 feet, suggests appearance of Mars in small telescope.

eyepiece allows comfortable viewing of objects high overhead.

In attempting to locate faint objects, especially, form the habit of estimating distances in terms of degrees, and of using the vicinity of the celestial pole as the key to directions. Distances can be estimated easily with the help of the finder (page 26).

A sector of sky seen in the finder or eyepiece is magnified as well as inverted. It differs from the same part of the sky as seen by the unaided eye. The beginner may find this confusing, but sighting becomes much easier with practice.

Making the Most of Eyesight

Observing with a telescope is a constant test of eyesight. What we can see, and how well we see it, depends not only upon the capacity of our eyes but also upon our skill in using them.

A good observer does not stare through the telescope; he takes quick

glances. Long looking causes fatigue and loss of visual sensitivity. A seasoned planetary observer may watch half the night for those few seconds when the atmosphere may become calm enough to allow a good view of some delicate detail, such as a cloud or a "canal" on Mars. But for him, too, rests for the eyes are essential.

When looking into an eyepiece, keep both eyes open. That means less fatigue for both eyes. You soon learn to concentrate on what the observing eye sees.

When seeking a very faint object in the field, or very faint details on an object, look a little to the side. Averted vision makes use of the more sensitive parts of the retina.

When comparing star magnitudes, variable star observers keep in mind that the eye is particularly sensitive to red. Red builds up on the retina as light builds up on photographic film. A red star, looked at steadily, seems to get brighter.

Never look at the Sun without proper precautions! (See pages 49-51.)

Handling Star Charts

The first experiences of a beginner in handling star charts at the telescope may be confusing and exasperating. The star field on the chart never looks exactly like the same field as seen through the finder or eyepiece. The two fields are likely to differ in scale. In the telescope the observer probably sees more stars than appear on the chart at hand. Finally, depending on the type of instrument and the orientation of its parts, the field as seen in the eyepiece may be reversed or inverted, or both. Some telescopes change the field in such a way that, to use the chart, we must look at its reverse side while holding it against a light.

Even the experienced observer sometimes becomes confused, but the beginner should not get discouraged. With a little experimenting he soon learns what happens to a star field in his instrument.

The method that usually works is simple: Look at the star chart and choose a bright star near the celestial object being sought. Using the finder, point the telescope at this star. Look into the eyepiece, identify the star, notice the figure it forms (triangle,

Harvard Obs.
Eta Carinae region: From this area of southern heavens comes much "radio noise," which is picked up by radio telescopes. Area is interesting to explore with optical telescopes also.

arc, etc.) with neighboring stars, and then hold the chart so that the figure there is in the same position as in the eyepiece.

Holding a star chart: In northern hemisphere, when observer is facing east, "N" side of chart is toward his left, in direction of north celestial pole. When facing south, "N" side is up. Facing north, "N" side is up or down depending on whether field is above or below pole. Facing west, north end of chart is toward right. In southern hemisphere, same procedure is followed, except that when facing south, observer holds chart so "S" side is toward pole. Text on these pages explains problem of how to hold chart at telescope.

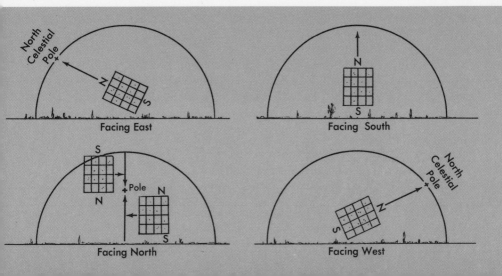

Southern Cross and Coalsack: Pattern of stars and dark nebula, suggesting "hole" in sky, are well-known southern-hemisphere objects, visible to unaided eye. They are exciting in wide-field telescope.

STAR CHARTS AND SETTING CIRCLES

Star charts are the astronomer's maps of the sky. With them he locates stars and other objects whose positions on the celestial sphere change little from year to year. On them he plots courses of Sun, planets, and other objects whose positions change more noticeably. Like maps of Earth's surface, star charts are prepared according to different scales. They show varying amounts of detail.

The charts on pages 114-123 are limited mostly to stars and other objects that can be seen with unaided eye and binoculars. The limit of these charts is, for the most part, about 5th magnitude. Special charts showing all the stars that can be seen with small telescopes have to be much more detailed; some include objects to a magnitude of 13 or 14. A full set of charts detailed enough to show all stars visible in binoculars alone can fill a small atlas.

Star Names and Designations

The bright stars on most charts are designated by Greek letters:

α	Alpha	ι	Iota	ρ	Rho
β	Beta	κ	Kappa	σ	Sigma
γ	Gamma	λ	Lambda	τ	Tau
δ	Delta	μ	Mu	υ	Upsilon
ϵ	Epsilon	ν	Nu	ϕ	Phi
ζ	Zeta	ξ	Xi	χ	Chi
η	Eta	o	Omicron	ψ	Psi
θ	Theta	π	Pi	ω	Omega

Except for a few examples such as Castor and Pollux, in Gemini, the brightest star in a constellation is given the letter α, the next brightest β, and so on.

Ancient sky observers gave names to the stars. Our modern charts retain the Greek letter designations and name only the brightest stars, such as Sirius, Procyon, Arcturus, Betelgeuse. To identify a star, we may simply use its name, such as Betelgeuse, which everyone knows is in the constellation Orion. However, if we designate the star as α, we write or say α Orionis, using the Latin genitive of the constellation name.

Sky Coordinates

Most star charts (such as those in this book) have a grillwork of vertical and horizontal lines, indicating right ascension and declination. These correspond to the geographer's lines of longitude and latitude.

The lines of right ascension are drawn between the celestial poles, and the lines of declination are drawn around the celestial sphere parallel to the celestial equator. Just as the location of any city on Earth can be pinpointed by stating its longitude and latitude, so the location of any object on the celestial sphere can be pinpointed by its right ascension and declination.

Declination, or distance from the celestial equator, is measured in degrees and minutes of arc. Declination north of the celestial equator is indicated by a plus (+) sign; south, by a minus (−) sign.

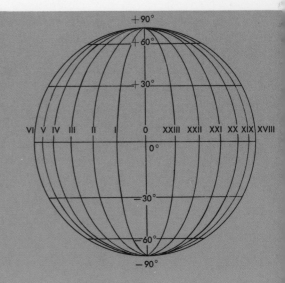

Right ascension and declination: Celestial sphere is mapped by means of lines indicating right ascension and declination. Lines of right ascension correspond to meridians, or lines of longitude, on Earth. Lines of declination correspond to lines of latitude. This diagram represents only half of celestial sphere, as seen from center; other half would show lines of right ascension from VI to XVIII.

Right ascension is measured in hours, minutes, and (if necessary) seconds, from 0 to 24 hours. It is measured eastward from a meridian that passes between the celestial poles and through the vernal equinox. The vernal equinox is the point where the sun crosses the celestial equator in its apparent northward journey in March each year.

The right ascension ("RA") and declination ("Dec") of an object can be written very simply, in the form of what astronomers call "coordinates," thus:

	RA	Dec
α Canis Majoris (Sirius)	6ʰ 43ᵐ	−16° 39′
α Orionis (Betelgeuse)	5ʰ 52ᵐ	+ 7° 24′

When the coordinates of any sky object are known, the object can be located easily by reference to star maps. This is true whether the object is a star, a planet, or any other subject of interest. Likewise, when any object is seen that does not appear on a star map (a comet, for example), we can determine its approximate coordinates by checking its position in relation to stars that do appear on the map. Coordinates also tell us where an object is in the heavens at different times of the year, and they make possible a precise, convenient way of using equatorial telescopes.

The coordinates of any star, star cluster, or nebula can be read from a star map simply by looking at the lines of right ascension and declina-

Looking north: If lines of right ascension and declination were "printed" on sky, observer in northern hemisphere, looking northward, would see this pattern. As Earth rotates, "wheel" of sky appears to turn counterclockwise and "hours" increase clockwise. In diagram for southern hemisphere, "wheel" would turn clockwise, and "hours" would increase counterclockwise.

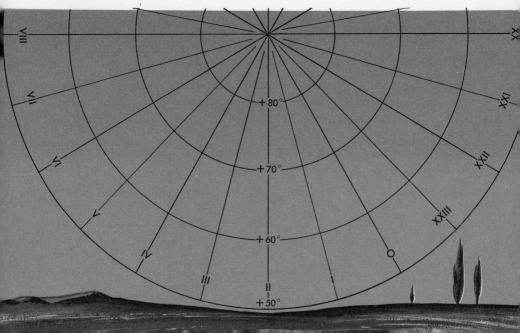

Looking south: Observer in northern hemisphere, looking south, would see this different pattern of coordinate lines. Motion of stars is from left to right; south celestial pole is below horizon. In diagram for southern-hemisphere observer, hours would increase from left to right, and north celestial pole would be below horizon.

tion. Coordinates of most of these objects change little over periods of years. But coordinates of planets, comets, and other objects in the solar system, which are relatively near us, do change regularly. They must therefore be obtained from almanacs and other up-to-date publications.

Using Coordinates

Suppose we want to have a look at the star Fomalhaut. We don't know what constellation it is in, but we do know its right ascension is $22^h 55^m$, and its declination $-29° 53'$. We find a star chart (page 120) with lines of right ascension and declination near to the coordinates of Fomalhaut. On this chart Fomalhaut is found easily in the constellation Piscis Austrinus. Then, with the help of the chart, if necessary, we find the constellation in the sky and identify Fomalhaut.

Now let us imagine we have spotted a dim comet in the constellation Cassiopeia, and we want to report it. Noting the position of the comet with reference to stars in the constellation, we plot the position as precisely as possible on a star chart. Then, by reference to the lines of right ascension and declination, we determine what the coordinates of the comet are. The discovery of the object can then be reported with a fair degree of accuracy, depending on the scale of the map used.

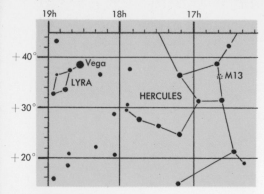

Finding M13: Section of map illustrates how bright stars can be used for locating faint objects.

Coordinates and Setting Circles

Many equatorial telescopes are equipped with setting circles. With these we can make direct use of coordinates at the telescope, if it has been set up properly (see pages 28-29).

The so-called hour circle corresponds to right ascension; it is marked for hours and minutes. The other circle, which indicates declination, is marked for degrees and minutes of arc.

To illustrate one way of using circles, suppose you are seeking that faint star cluster M13, in Hercules. Your star atlas shows Vega as the nearest bright star; so you use Vega as the starting point. The chart gives the following coordinates:

	RA	Dec
Vega	18^h 35^m	+38° 44'
M13	16^h 40^m	+36° 33'

Subtracting, you see that the distance from Vega to M13 is 2° 11' in Dec southward, and 1^h 55^m in RA westward.

You now get Vega in the center of the field and clamp the RA axis. Watching the Dec circle, you move the tube 2° 11' southward. The Dec axis is then clamped. Next, you unclamp the RA axis. Watching the hour circle, you move the tube 1^h 55^m in RA westward. That should bring you to M13.

This method usually works well enough to bring the desired object into the field of a low-power eyepiece —say, a 1-inch. If the telescope is properly pointed, a higher-powered eyepiece can be used, if desired.

Another method of using setting circles involves the use of sidereal time. The sidereal time (ST) at any moment is equal to the RA of any

Setting circles: When properly set by means of circles, telescope points at desired spot in heavens.

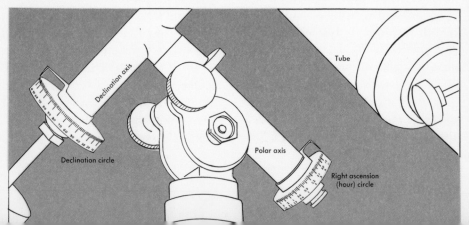

Elusive objects: In time-exposure photos made by observatories, nebulas such as this (M81 in Ursa Major) are prominent and well defined. In small telescope they are usually very faint, and use of setting circles helps to find them.

Mt. Wilson and Palomar Obs.

star that is on the observer's meridian at that moment (see page 105).

To determine the sidereal time, pick out some familiar star on or near the equator whose RA is known. The star should be slightly east of the meridian. Point the telescope due south and clamp it in declination equal to the Dec of the star. Watch the field of view, and when the star is observed in the center set your watch or a clock to agree with the RA of the star. This will serve as a sidereal clock for the evening.

When the circles are properly adjusted, the RA circle will read 0^h when the telescope is pointed due south. Then, to find any star, it is necessary only to find out how far the star is from the meridian; that is, its hour angle (HA), east or west. The HA can be obtained by simply finding the difference between the ST and the RA of the star. (Remember: sidereal time is reckoned continuously from 0 to 24 hours.) If RA is greater than ST, the HA is east of the meridian. If ST is greater than RA, the HA is west of the meridian.

Assume you want to sight the star Algieba (γ Leonis) in the constellation Leo. You have the following information:

RA $10^h 17^m$ Dec 20° 06′   ST $07^h 37^m$

Since RA is greater than ST, we subtract ST from RA and get HA $2^h 40^m$ east of the meridian. That is, we learn that the star is $2^h 40^m$ east of the meridian.

Now assume ST is $13^h 50^m$, which is $3^h 33^m$ greater than RA. This means the HA (or star) is that far west of the meridian.

Once you have the HA, clamp the telescope in the declination of γ Leonis (+20°06′). Then unclamp the RA axis and turn the tube east or west (as the case may be) to the desired angle on the RA circle, and there is Algieba.

A different method of finding an object is possible if the telescope has a movable hour circle marked from 0^h to 24^h. Get a bright star in the center of the field. Turn the circle to read its RA. To find the desired object, just turn the telescope until the circle reads the RA of this object.

THE MOON

The Moon is our nearest neighbor, except for certain asteroids and man-made satellites. This bleak, airless sphere is about 2,160 miles in diameter, and revolves around Earth at an average distance of some 238,857 miles, completing one revolution in about 27 days. The lunar orbit is an ellipse, not a true circle; so the distance of the Moon from Earth changes.

Since the Moon rotates on its axis in the same time it takes to revolve around Earth, the lunar hemisphere visible to us remains about the same. Librations (apparent tilting due to the Moon's motions with respect to Earth) make a total of about 59 per cent of the lunar surface visible.

The Light of the Moon

Sunlight falls on the Moon as it does on Earth. But the Moon has no atmosphere to filter the fierce rays. The lunar surface in daylight, therefore, gets intensely hot — something like 250°F., or hotter than boiling water. (The dark side probably gets to 112°F. below zero!) What we call "moonlight" is simply sunlight which the Moon is reflecting toward Earth.

Except during lunar eclipses, a full half of the Moon is always lighted by the Sun. But we see this full half only when Earth is between Sun and Moon—the phase called full Moon. We see none of the lighted half when the Moon is between Earth and Sun— the phase called new Moon. When the Moon is not in line with Earth and Sun, we see part of the lighted half.

Just after new Moon, we see a thin bright crescent. The rest of the disk is faintly lighted—an effect called "the old Moon in the new Moon's arms." The faint light is light reflected from Earth to the Moon's dark side, and is known as earthshine.

The Moon rises about 50 minutes later each night on the average, but the actual time from month to month

The Moon: Composite picture, showing details with exquisite clarity, was made by combining photos taken at first and last quarter. Photo of Moon at full phase would show less detail.

Lick Obs.

Sky companions: Moon and Venus appear together over Denver in picture made by alert photographer. Note Earthshine on Moon.

Harry Brauneis

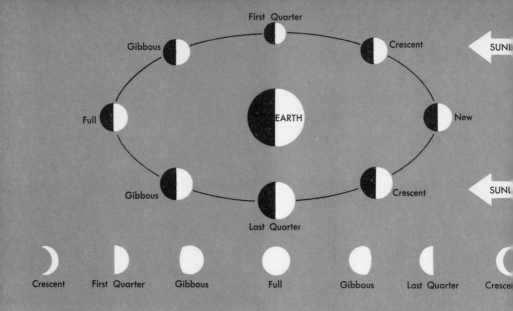

Moon phases: At all times, a full hemisphere of Moon is lighted by Sun. How much of lighted area we see depends on position of Moon in its orbit. In northern hemisphere, as diagrammed here, Moon appears to "grow" from right to left; in southern hemisphere it "grows" from left to right.

varies considerably. At times in the fall, for several evenings near full Moon, moonrise is only about 20 minutes later each night, giving us moonlight in the early evening over a longer period than usual. So we have "Harvest Moon" and "Hunter's Moon." Harvest Moon is the full phase occurring nearest the autumnal equinox (about September 23). The next full phase after Harvest Moon is Hunter's Moon.

The lunar pathway stays near the ecliptic, or path of the Sun. However, while the Sun rides high in summer and low in winter, the Moon rides low in summer and high in winter.

At the full phase, the lunar disk may take odd shapes as it rises or sets, particularly when seen through a dense or smoky atmosphere. Sometimes it may look oval.

Atmospheric conditions cause the Moon to show changing colors. If the high atmosphere contains clouds of minute ice crystals, the lunar halo may be seen.

Pointers for Observers

The Moon is one of the most satisfying objects for the small telescope and also for binoculars. The best time to observe is the period from last quarter to first quarter. Then there is less glare. The shadows of the mountains and in the craters are longest and set off the rugged landscape in sharp relief. Often the Moon can be observed to advantage during daylight hours.

When beyond the crescent stage, the Moon reflects considerable light. For prolonged telescopic observing a filter should be used over the eye-

42

piece, or a filter cap placed over the objective, or the area of the objective reduced by placing over it a cardboard cap with a hole of the desired size. (See pages 50 and 107.)

Another way to cut down glare is to use an eyepiece of high enough power so that only part of the Moon is seen in the field of view. Then less light reaches the eye. Higher magnification, of course, increases the effect of atmospheric turbulence, and the image tends to become poorer.

After a period of lunar observing, the sensitivity of the eye to fainter objects is much reduced. Plan observing sessions accordingly.

Some mountain ranges, seas, and craters can be seen even with binoculars. Much more can be seen with a small telescope. With a 3- or 4-inch instrument, use a low power—30 to 100x. Don't use power beyond what atmospheric conditions allow.

For serious lunar work, a 6- or 8-inch telescope should be used, with a power up to 300x or 400x. Then you can observe clearly details that are only a half mile across.

Lunar halo: Refraction of moonlight by ice crystals in high atmosphere produces this spectacle. Usual halo is 22° wide. Sometimes a 46° halo is seen.

The Lunar Landscape

The waterless lunar landscape is on a gigantic scale. Many of its mountain peaks are higher, and many of its craters larger, than any on Earth. Vast flat areas—the maria, or "seas" —are visible. Great mountain ranges such as the Apennines, Alps, and Caucasus, are always of interest. Numerous craters deserve special attention—Plato and Archimedes, Copernicus and Tycho and Kepler.

Atmospheric effects: When near horizon, Moon may appear reddish and flattened. At this time, sunlight reflected by Moon to Earth has longer path through atmosphere. Red rays penetrate atmosphere more easily than other colors. Bending of light by atmosphere causes flattened effect.

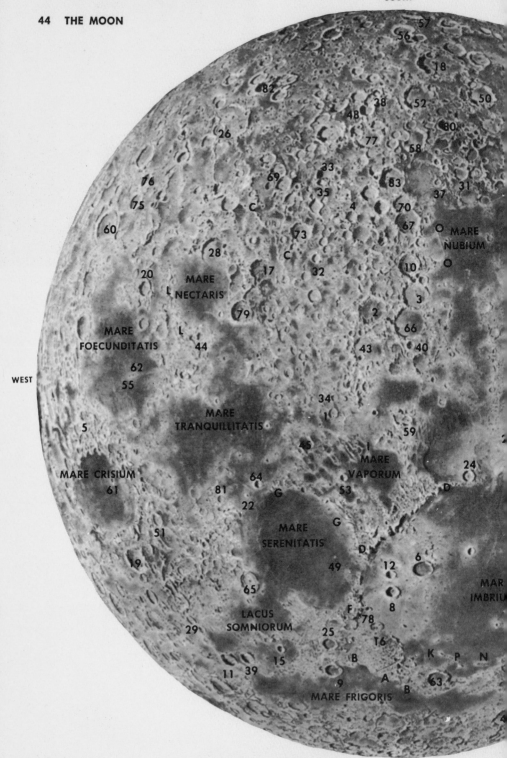

57
56
18
82
38 52 50
48 80
26 77 58
33 83 31
69 35 70 37
C 4 67 O MARE
75 73 70 NUBIUM
60 28 10 O
20 17 C 32 3
MARE 2 66
NECTARIS 79 43 40
L
MARE L 44 34
FOECUNDITATIS 1
62 46 59
55 I
MARE MARE
TRANQUILLITATIS VAPORUM
5 64 24
MARE CRISIUM 81 G 53 D
61 22 G
51 D
19 49 12 6
65 8
LACUS F 78
SOMNIORUM 25 T6
29 B K P N
15 A
11 39 9 B 63
MARE FRIGORIS

MAR
IMBRIU

MARE
SERENITATIS

WEST

THE MOON

Mountains and Valleys

A	Alpine Valley	I	Hyginus Cleft
B	Alps	J	Jura Mts.
C	Altai	K	Pico
D	Apennine Mts.	L	Pyrenees
E	Carpathian	M	Riphaeus
F	Caucasus	N	Straight Range
G	Haemus	O	Straight Wall
H	Harbinger	P	Teneriffe

Craters

1	Agrippa	43	Hipparchus
2	Albategnius	44	Isidorus
3	Alphonsus	45	Julius Caesar
4	Apianus	46	Kepler
5	Apollonius	47	Lambert
6	Archimedes	48	Licetus
7	Aristarchus	49	Linné
8	Aristillus	50	Longomontanus
9	Aristoteles	51	Macrobius
10	Arzachel	52	Maginus
11	Atlas	53	Manilius
12	Autolycus	54	Mercator
13	Bayer	55	Messier
14	Bullialdus	56	Moretus
15	Bürg	57	Newton
16	Cassini	58	Orontius
17	Catharina	59	Pallas
18	Clavius	60	Petavius
19	Cleomedes	61	Picard
20	Colombo	62	Pickering, W.H.
21	Copernicus	63	Plato
22	Dawes	64	Plinius
23	Encke	65	Posidonius
24	Eratosthenes	66	Ptolomaeus
25	Eudoxus	67	Purbach
26	Fabricius	68	Pythagoras
27	Flamsteed	69	Rabbi Levi
28	Fracastorius	70	Regiomontanus
29	Franklin	71	Reinhold
30	Gassendi	72	Riccioli
31	Gauricus	73	Sacrobosco
32	Geber	74	Schiller
33	Gemma Frisius	75	Snellius
34	Godin	76	Stevinus
35	Goodacre	77	Stöfler
36	Grimaldi	78	Theaetetus
37	Hell	79	Theophilus
38	Heraclitus	80	Tycho
39	Hercules	81	Vitruvius
40	Herschel	82	Vlacq
41	Herschel, J.	83	Walter
42	Hevelius		

MARE
MORUM
30
36
27
OCEANUS
72
EAST
42
23
46
PROCELLARUM
7
H

Copernicus: This mountain-ringed plain (right) has eight peaks, one 2400 ft. high. Note rays around Copernicus. Note "drowned" craters (high center).

Apennines: Here is part of splendid range which runs 450 miles around west side of Mare Imbrium. Big crater is Archimedes, 70 miles wide.

Tycho: A mountain-ringed plain like Copernicus, Tycho is 54 miles wide. Rays reach hundreds of miles.

There are the long, straight cliffs; deep, narrow, or crooked valleys; wide cracks sometimes extending hundreds of miles; light-colored streaks or rays extending from some of the craters, the most striking of which are those from Tycho.

Names on the Moon

In 1650, the astronomer Riccioli produced the first map of the Moon. He is said to have originated the system of naming that we use today. The great plains or flat areas are called "seas" (Mare Nubium, Sea of Clouds; Mare Imbrium, Sea of Rains; and so forth). Most of the mountain ranges bear some resemblance to those on Earth, such as the Alps and Apennines, and are named after them. Conspicuous craters bear the names of ancient philosophers and astronomers—Plato, Archimedes, Kepler. Smaller craters honor more modern astronomers. Various details refer to counterparts on Earth—Bays and Gulfs, Capes and Lakes.

There has been much imagining and arguing about the lunar landscape. Typical are such questions as: How did the mountains form? Were the craters in the "seas" caused by meteors? What are the "rays"? Are the so-called impact flashes meteor hits? Are there changes taking place on the surface now? Are the "seas" old lava flows?

Many observers regularly train their telescopes on the Moon to watch for impacts. Others look for "bridges" and other peculiar structures. Some study the rays.

We are getting closer to that day when rocket ships will carry men to the Moon. Sky observers will then have still more exciting days and nights of lunar observation.

Eclipses

Once in a while, when at the full phase, the Moon passes through Earth's shadow, either partially or completely, creating one of nature's glorious phenomena: an eclipse. In any one year there may be two or even three lunar eclipses, or none.

A total lunar eclipse lasts as much as 1 hour and 40 minutes—much longer than a total solar eclipse. There is plenty of time to see it and observe the ever-changing colors. During an eclipse, familiar lunar features take on a new appearance.

In a total solar eclipse, the disk of the Sun is completely hidden by the Moon. But in a lunar eclipse, the disk of the Moon can still be seen, even in Earth's shadow. Some of the sunlight passing through Earth's atmosphere is refracted so that it falls on the Moon, giving it a coppery hue.

Lick Obs.
Pickering: Here, some think, a meteor may have smashed through a mountain range, making a tunnel.

Lick Obs.
Straight Wall: This steep escarpment (near center), about 80 miles long, probably results from fault in Moon's crust. "Drowned" craters (lower right) were perhaps filled by lava flows.

Lick Obs.
Three lunar features: Alpine Valley (groove at left), 80 miles long and 11,500 ft. deep, may have been cut by meteor. Big crater (center), 60 miles wide, is Plato. Straight Range (corner at lower right) has a dozen peaks, stretches about 45 miles.

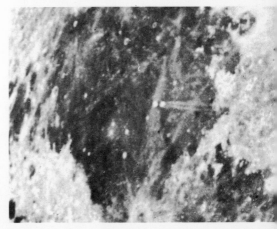

47

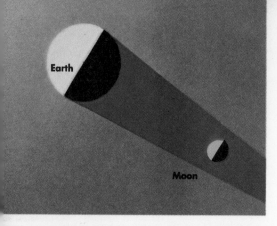

Lunar eclipse: In this diagram, sunlight comes from left. Moon is eclipsed as it comes into Earth's shadow. Shadow is not completely dark, because some sunlight is refracted into it by Earth's atmosphere. Refracted light gives Moon disk reddish tint.

TOTAL LUNAR ECLIPSES,
1964-1970

1964	Jun. 25	1967	Oct. 18
1964	Dec. 19	1968	Apr. 13
1965	None	1968	Oct. 6
1966	None	1969	None
1967	Apr. 24	1970	None

Occultations

Every now and then the Moon passes in front of a star or planet, hiding it for a short time. This event is called an occultation and is of great interest to mapmakers.

If the time of disappearance and the time of reappearance are accurately timed by observers who are at different locations on Earth, the data can be used to determine the exact distances between those locations. The exact positions of continents, remote islands, and other parts of the globe are checked in this way.

Many experienced observers do occultation work as their contribution to astronomy. A small telescope, a short-wave radio, and a good watch or stopwatch are the essentials.

Accurate time signals can be obtained from Radio Station WWV. Dates when occultations will occur can be found in *Sky and Telescope* magazine.

Things to Do

1. Observe occultations.
2. Make detailed drawings of Moon's surface.
3. Observe eclipses.
4. Watch sunrise over the lunar mountains.
5. Watch the ever-changing appearance of several particular lunar features, night after night.
6. Take photographs (see pages 95-99).
7. Time the Moon's rising and setting times, over a lunar month.
8. Study the rays.
9. Watch for impacts.

Occultation: Jupiter and satellites appear after occultation by Moon. (Based on Griffith Obs. photos)

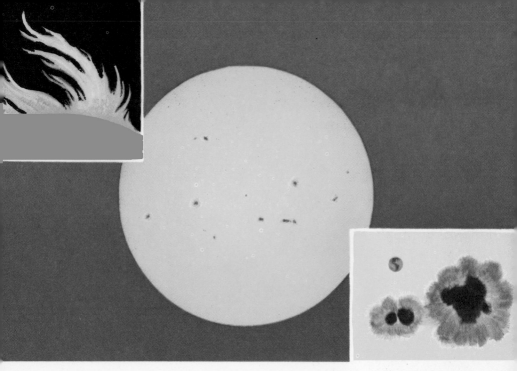

Features of Sun: Surface, or photosphere, is marked with sunspots which change in size, number, and position. Inset, lower right, compares size of sunspot group with Earth. Inset at upper left shows gigantic tongues of incandescent gases, called prominences, at Sun's surface.

THE SUN

The Sun, like other stars, is a giant sphere of incandescent gases. Its diameter is about 864,000 miles, or over 100 times the diameter of Earth. Its gravitational attraction governs the movement of all the planets. So great is its size that if Earth were placed at its center, the Moon would orbit about halfway between Earth and the surface of the Sun.

Earth revolves around the Sun in a path that is an ellipse, not a perfect circle. Hence our distance from the Sun changes slightly from month to month. Earth is farthest from the Sun in July (94.4 million miles), and nearest in January (91.4 million).

Never look at the Sun without protection for the eyes.

Many telescopes come equipped with special filters, eyepieces, or prisms for use in direct observation of the Sun. Some telescopes are fitted with an adjustable screen so that the Sun's image can be projected.

If your telescope has no such protective devices, they can be made or bought. Generally it is better to buy the special eyepieces, prisms, or filters than to take a chance on home-made devices.

The Sun cap, which is a filter mounted in an adapter to fit over the eyepiece, can be used with 2½- to 3-

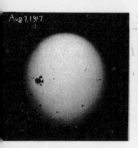
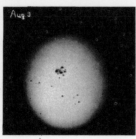
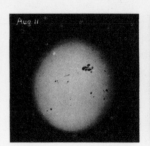
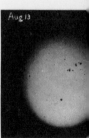

Yerkes Obs.

Proving the Sun's rotation: Photos reveal gradual movement of sunspots across Sun's disk.

inch telescopes. For larger instruments, special eyepieces designed for the purpose are necessary.

Some observers using large instruments reduce the aperture by fitting a cap over the objective. The cap consists of a snug-fitting cardboard disk with a hole of the size desired cut in the center. But cutting down the aperture also reduces definition in small details, and it does not prevent the eyepiece from getting hot.

Do not observe through balsam or gelatin filters. The balsam and gelatin can melt, and eye damage can happen quickly.

Refractor and reflector equipped for solar observation: Image of Sun is projected harmlessly on to screen, which can be moved easily to position that gives image of size desired. Focusing is done with eyepiece. Strength of sunlight can be cut down by placing diaphragm over upper end of tube. Observer must not look through finder or eyepiece except with solar filter.

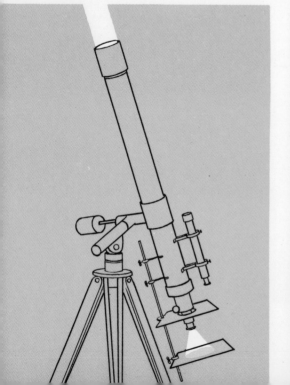
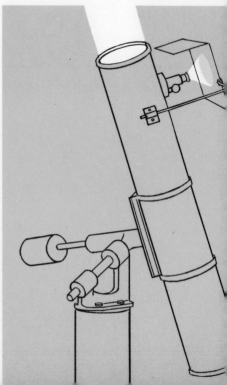

High power is not required to see sunspots—60x to 100x is usually sufficient. Small telescopes will do. Binoculars (use filters over the objectives!) will reveal the larger spots.

The safest way to observe the Sun is to project its image onto a screen held in back of the eyepiece. A simple device, easily made, is shown here. It allows several persons to observe at the same time.

Don't try to set the telescope on the Sun by looking through the finder or by gazing up the tube. That is risky and awkward. If you are using a screen, aim the tube by watching its shadow on the screen. If no screen is being used, hold a card up behind the eyepiece.

For visual observation without optical aid, an overexposed film, or processed unexposed Kodachrome film, gives satisfactory protection.

The best time to look at the Sun is

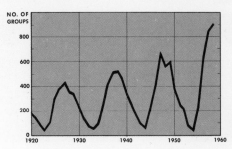

Sunspot cycle: Sunspots show rapid increase in number, then slow decline. From peak to peak, time is about 11 years.

in the morning, before its full heating effect is felt. Then the atmosphere is steadier.

Sunspots

The Sun is especially interesting when it has spots, and particularly when these are increasing. Sunspot numbers are given in several publications, including *Sky and Telescope*.

Sunspots vary from specks to giants 90,000 miles across. The largest can be seen without optical aid.

Solar eclipses: Map shows paths traced by Moon's shadow during solar eclipses, 1955-1986.

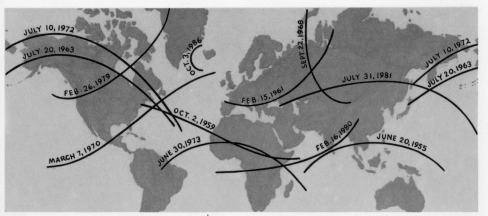

Annular eclipse: Moon is so far from Earth that its *apparent* size is smaller than apparent size of Sun. Hence it does not completely hide Sun; a ring (annulus) of Sun surrounds it.

Total eclipse: Moon is near enough to Earth so that its apparent size is slightly greater than apparent size of Sun. Hence lunar disk can completely hide Sun.

These odd features are disturbances of great extent and violence on the Sun, and are often referred to as "storms." Each has a dark core, the umbra, and an outer gray band, the penumbra. Because the spots are cooler than the surrounding surface, they appear darker.

The spots change in size and position from day to day. Some appear and disappear in a day or two. Others can be observed crossing the solar disk, taking about 14 days for the journey. This apparent crossing is due to the Sun's rotation.

The number of spots varies from just a few in a year to as many as 150 in one day. They come in cycles, the period from one maximum to the next maximum being about 11 years.

Through a telescope the Sun's surface has a granular or mottled appearance. Near the spots, and particularly toward the edge of the disk, whitish spots may be seen, called "faculae." Other phenomena that can be seen at times are flares, which are bright flashes near the spots. These are rare but worth looking for.

All of the features of the Sun represent great activity. Increasing solar activity is closely allied to increasing auroral displays, and generally there is interference with short-wave radio and television. Whenever you observe increased activity on the Sun, or notice unusual interference with radio and TV, watch for auroral displays a day or so later.

Solar Eclipses

Solar eclipses have always excited mankind. Superstition has clothed them with strange and terrifying meanings. Science has looked forward to eclipses as occasions when certain solar phenomena, such as prominences and the corona, which are ordinarily invisible, could be observed. Today the unsuperstitious observer looks forward to an eclipse eagerly, and so does the professional astronomer, although he can use the coronagraph to produce an artificial eclipse in the observatory. Nature's own display remains unrivaled in its splendor.

A *total* solar eclipse occurs when the Moon is directly in line between Earth and Sun. If the Moon is not exactly in line, only a partial eclipse occurs. An *annular* eclipse happens when the Moon, even though directly in line with Earth and Sun, is far enough away from Earth so that the dark central part of its shadow cannot reach Earth.

There are at least two total eclipses a year, and sometimes as many as five, but few people have a chance to see them. Solar eclipses are very brief, and the paths along which they can be seen are narrow. Any eclipse is worth traveling far to see, even though it may last only about 7½ minutes at most.

Among the features of a total eclipse are the so-called Baily's Beads. These are seen just as the Moon's black disk covers the last thin crescent of the Sun. Sunlight shining between the mountains at the Moon's edge looks like sparkling beads.

The Diamond Ring effect is a fleeting flash of light immediately preceding and following totality.

Stages of solar eclipse: Series of exposures by news photographer makes superb picture and suggests possibilities for camera-minded sky observers.

Roy E. Swan, Minneapolis Star

At the time of totality, the observer with a small telescope can see the Sun's prominences—long, flame-like tongues of incandescent gases, appearing around the edge of the Moon's disk.

Also during totality we see the glorious filmy corona. Its glowing gases stretch out millions of miles from the blacked-out Sun.

Preparing for an Eclipse

To get the most out of the few minutes of an eclipse, preparations must be made long in advance.

Decide what you want to do and get ready. Prepare equipment carefully. Study the charts that appear in newspapers and other publications to determine the path of the Moon's shadow. Try to pick a good location near the area where the eclipse will last the longest, and along the center of the shadow's path. Also, if possible, find a spot at a high elevation so that you can get an uninterrupted view to the horizon, in the direction of the path of the shadow. There is little room to choose from, for the shadow is only about 100 miles wide.

Prior to totality, the onrush of the Moon's shadow can be seen. Have a white sheet on the ground, and just as totality begins, try to observe on it the so-called shadow bands—light and dark bands only a few inches across and a few feet apart.

Last but not least, look for stars in the sky during totality, and look for Mercury. Look at the shadows and sunlight filtering through the trees during the progress of the eclipse. Notice the effect of darkness on birds and animals. Carry a thermometer and watch the temperature. And by all means use your camera!

Drama of Sun and Moon: As solar eclipse nears totality, last crescent of Sun disappears. Glints of sunlight at Moon's rugged edge produce Baily's Beads (left) or Diamond Ring effect (middle). With beginning of totality (right), shimmering corona appears. Totality seldom lasts more than a minute or two.

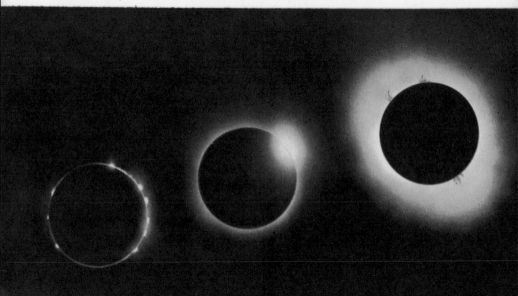

RAINBOWS, AURORAS AND
ZODIACAL LIGHT

When sunlight passes through a prism, the prism disperses the light, breaking it up into all colors from red to violet—called the spectrum. In the same way, sunlight is affected by passage through Earth's atmosphere.

Observe the changing blues in the sky, caused by the scattering of blue light. This is more noticeable in the early morning or as the Sun is setting.

Notice how the changing density and composition of our atmosphere—how smoke, dust, and other particles —make colorful sunrises and sunsets. Watch how the atmosphere, by scat-

tering light, gives us the phenomenon of twilight.

Just after sunset or before sunrise, watch for the "Sun pillar"—a brilliant column of light of the same color as the sunset or sunrise.

Of all the color effects of sunlight in our atmosphere, the best known are rainbows. These are produced as rays of sunlight strike droplets of water in the air. The droplets act as prisms, dispersing the light and separating the colors.

Rainbows appear opposite the Sun. Seen from the ground, a rainbow is

Zodiacal light: Glow near horizon, along ecliptic, may be reflection of sunlight from meteoric material.

always less than half a circle. The length of the bow depends upon the Sun's angle. Seen from an airplane, rainbows often are complete circles.

A single rainbow has red on the outside, violet inside. Occasionally a second bow forms outside the first, with its colors reversed. Rarely, as many as five bows are seen.

Sometimes the Sun appears to have a bright light or ghostlike sphere on each side of it. These are commonly called "Sun dogs." They are always associated with a halo.

The *aurora borealis* (northern lights) in the northern hemisphere, and *aurora australis* (southern lights) in the southern hemisphere, are probably the result of charged particles entering Earth's atmosphere. These particles may originate in sunspots, for at a time of great sunspot activity auroral displays are likely too.

Auroras are most frequent in higher latitudes. Contrary to general opinion, they may be seen at times anywhere in the United States. Northern lights have been seen as far south as

Curtain aurora: No painting or photograph can fully suggest its shimmering, ghostly movement.

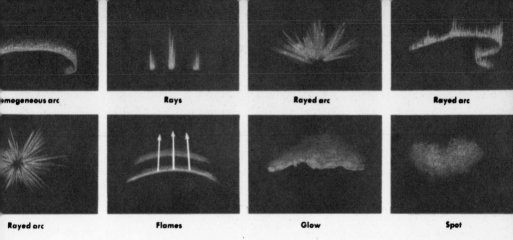

Homogeneous arc   Rays   Rayed arc   Rayed arc

Rayed arc   Flames   Glow   Spot

Types of Auroras

Mexico, and southern lights as far north as Australia and New Zealand.

Look toward the pole that is nearer you. Generally, auroras are more spectacular after midnight, but they may be visible earlier.

No special equipment is required —just good eyes. But auroras are good subjects for the camera fan, both in black and white and in color.

Auroras often look like flimsy clouds or distant fog. Many persons have seen them without recognizing them. Look twice at such clouds when seen in the direction of the pole. Real clouds hide the brighter stars; auroras do not.

Watch for any change in a hazy glow near the horizon. It may become a well-defined arc, then break up into rays like searchlight beams. Sometimes arcs and rays flash up and quickly disappear.

Auroras come in many forms and colors—red and green most frequently. Particularly impressive are the irregular vibrating or pulsating bands or arcs, also called draperies. The auroras called flames may reach high overhead like gigantic wind-blown ribbons.

Another spectacular form is the corona, or "crown," formed by rays that seem to radiate from a point near the zenith.

The Zodiacal light and Gegenschein are phenomena of the night sky that are not commonly recognized. They are light reflected from minute particles—perhaps meteoric material—in the band of the Zodiac.

The Zodiacal light is a hazy band of light rising from the horizon along the ecliptic just after twilight in the west, or just before dawn in the east.

The Gegenschein, or "counterglow," is a brightening in the band of Zodiacal light at a point on the ecliptic opposite the Sun. Sometimes the Gegenschein may be seen when the Zodiacal light is invisible. The best time to look for it is about midnight and toward the south, near your meridian.

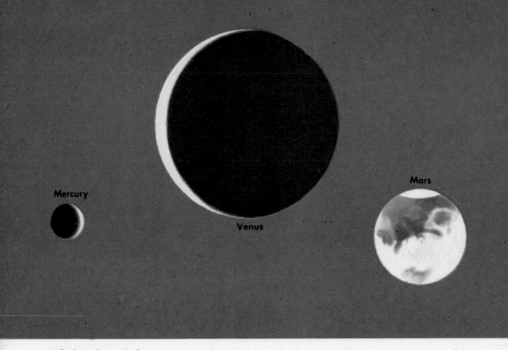

Mercury

Venus

Mars

Relative sizes of planets as seen from Earth under best conditions: Venus, Jupiter, and Saturn are large but shrouded in clouds. Venus and Mercury in "full" phase are very small disks showing hardly any

THE PLANETS AND ASTEROIDS

Every sky observer should become familiar with the constellations of the Zodiac. When we see in one of them a "star" that is not accounted for on a star chart, it is pretty sure to be a planet — particularly if it doesn't twinkle. Planets shine with a steady light.

In the telescope, planets are small disks—not mere points of light like stars. They vary in size, appearance, and apparent motion. All revolve about the Sun and shine by reflecting sunlight.

Inferior and Superior Planets

Those planets that revolve between Earth and Sun are called the inner, or

inferior, planets. Those that revolve beyond Earth are the outer, or superior, planets. The asteroids, also called planetoids or minor planets, do not follow the Zodiac as do the large planets.

At times a superior planet appears to have a retrograde motion. In its slow motion through a constellation, it appears to slow down and then go into reverse. After a few months the forward motion may be resumed again.

The planet does not actually reverse its motion. It only seems so because of changes in the relative positions of Earth and the planet as they move along in their orbits.

Jupiter

Saturn

Uranus

Neptune

detail. Uranus and Neptune are mere dots of light, and Pluto is entirely invisible except in large telescopes. Of all planets, only one to show a "landscape" is Mars. Painting shows apparent, not actual, relative sizes.

Morning and Evening Star

Mercury and Venus are the true morning and evening "stars," because their orbits lie between Earth and Sun. It is only just before sunrise and just after sunset, a few times a year, that Mercury can be seen. Venus is visible for longer periods before sunrise and after sunset, and sometimes in daylight.

Mars, Jupiter, and Saturn also are often referred to as morning or evening stars. This is when they dominate the sky in early morning or evening.

Locating the Planets

The positions of most stars, as shown on star charts, do not need to be corrected for decades. The posi-

tions of planets are changing constantly, and consequently are not printed on such charts. To find out where a planet is on a certain date, one must turn to a special table or list, as on page 61.

To locate Venus, Mars, Jupiter, and Saturn, you need to know only the name of the constellation in which the planet appears. These planets ordinarily are bright enough to be distinguished easily from the nearby stars. But the outer planets—Uranus, Neptune, and Pluto—are dimmer and thus harder to distinguish, and more exact information about their positions is required. This is available in astronomical publications (see page 113). Uranus and Neptune can be spotted in binoculars, if one knows

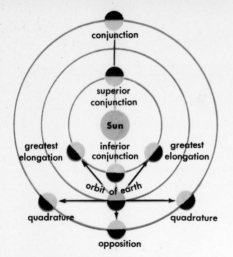

conjunction

superior
conjunction

Sun

greatest
elongation

inferior
conjunction

greatest
elongation

orbit of earth

quadrature

quadrature

opposition

Planet positions: Diagram demonstrates meaning of terms used to describe locations of planets with reference to Earth and Sun.

Opposition: Superior planet in line (or nearly so) with Earth and Sun; Earth in middle.

Quadrature: Superior planet at right angles to Earth and Sun.

Conjunction: Superior planet in line with Earth and Sun but beyond Sun.

Greatest elongation: Inferior planet at right angles with Earth and Sun.

Inferior conjunction: Inferior planet in line with, and between, Earth and Sun.

Superior conjunction: Inferior planet in line with Earth and Sun, and beyond Sun.

exactly where to look. But only a 12-inch telescope or better can pick up an object as faint as Pluto.

When to Look

All the planets except Mercury and Venus follow orbits outside Earth's orbit. Each of these outer planets is seen best when in opposition; that is, when Earth is directly between it and the Sun. Then the planet is closest to Earth and its face is fully lighted by the Sun.

Mercury and Venus follow orbits inside Earth's, and they are never in opposition. We see their faces fully lighted only when the Sun is between them and Earth; but then their disks are quite small. As celestial objects they appear brightest and largest at the time of greatest elongation, although then we see only part of their lighted side.

The time of greatest elongation is when the planet and the Sun, as seen by us, are at their greatest distance apart. This distance can be as much as 48° for Venus and 28° for Mercury.

The best time to observe planets is on moonless nights, or when they are opposite in the sky from the Moon, or when highest above the horizon. At or near full Moon, observing is not good for either planets or stars.

Observing Equipment

Features of the planets have been under close observation for a century. There has been much conjecture about them. Detailed study requires large, special, and expensive equipment; but there is much the sky observer can see and do with his small telescope. The brighter planets are excellent subjects.

Certain features can be observed with binoculars, such as the four large moons of Jupiter. With very powerful binoculars the phases of Venus and the rings of Saturn are barely discernible. For real planetary observing a 3- to 6-inch refractor or a 6- to 12-inch reflector is needed.

PLANET LOCATIONS, 1964-1970

For positions of Mercury, Uranus, Neptune, and Pluto, refer to *American Ephemeris and Nautical Almanac* or other yearly astronomical handbooks, or to *Sky and Telescope* magazine.

VENUS

Italic type indicates evening star; regular type indicates morning star. Dashes indicate Venus is too near Sun for observation. (Source: Planet Tables by Fred L. Whipple)

	JANUARY	APRIL	OCTOBER	DECEMBER
1964	*Aquarius*	*Taurus*	Taurus	Leo-Virgo
1965	Sagittarius	—	*Cancer-Leo*	*Ophiuchus*
1966	—	Aquarius	Taurus-Gemini	—
1967	—	*Taurus*	Leo	Leo
1968	Scorpius-Sagittarius	—	—	*Libra-Ophiuchus*
1969	*Aquarius-Pisces*	Pisces	Taurus	Virgo
1970	—	*Aries-Taurus*	Leo	*Libra*

MARS

1964	*Capricornus*	Pisces	Taurus	Leo
1965	Virgo	*Leo*	*Virgo*	Scorpius-Ophiuchus
1966	*Capricornus*	—	Taurus-Gemini	Leo
1967	Virgo	Virgo	*Virgo*	Ophiuchus
1968	*Aquarius*	*Aries*	Gemini	Leo
1969	Virgo-Libra	Ophiuchus	*Scorpius*	*Sagittarius*
1970	*Pisces*	*Taurus*	—	Virgo

JUPITER

1964	*Pisces*	—	Aries	Taurus
1965	*Aries*	*Taurus*	Taurus	Gemini
1966	*Taurus*	*Taurus*	Gemini	Cancer
1967	Cancer	*Gemini*	—	Leo
1968	Leo	*Leo*	*Leo*	Virgo
1969	Virgo	*Virgo*	*Virgo*	Virgo
1970	Virgo	Virgo	*Virgo*	—

SATURN

1964	*Capricornus*	Aquarius	Aquarius	*Aquarius*
1965	*Aquarius*	Aquarius	Aquarius	*Aquarius*
1966	*Aquarius*	Pisces	Pisces	*Pisces*
1967	*Pisces*	Pisces	Pisces	*Pisces*
1968	*Pisces*	Pisces	Pisces	Pisces
1969	*Pisces*	—	Aries	Aries
1970	*Aries*	—	Aries	Aries

Apparitions of Venus: Photos taken over two-month period show changes in apparent size and position.

Hans Pfleumer

THE PLANETS

	Mercury	Venus	Earth	Mars	Jupiter
Mean distance from Sun: astronomical units*	0.387	0.723	1.000*	1.524	5.203
million miles	35.96	67.20	92.90	141.54	483.32
Approximate distance from Earth: million miles	50 to 136	25 to 161	— — —	35 to 248	367 to 600
Diameter: miles	3,010	7,610	7,918	4,140	86,900
Period of revolution: Earth = 1 yr.	88.0 days	224.7 days	365.3 days	687.0 days	11.86 yrs.
Period of rotation: Earth = 1 day	88 days	30 days	23^h56^m	24^h37^m	$9^h50^m\pm$
Approximate diameter of disk: seconds of arc**	10.9	60.8	—	17.9	45.3
No. of moons	0	0	1	2	12
Visible in: 3-inch tel.	0	0	1	0	4
6-inch tel.	0	0	1	0	4
Magnitude range	−1.9 to +1.1	−4.4 to −3.3	— — —	−2.8 to +1.6	−2.5 to −1.4
Color	orange†	yellow†	—	red†	yellow†

*Astronomical unit = 92,897,000 miles (mean distance of Earth from Sun).
†Colors observed by unaided eye.
**Approximate mean diameter of Sun = 31′59″. Approximate mean diameter of Moon = 31′05″.

Most reflecting telescopes work at an f/6 or f/8 ratio—that is, the focal length of the primary mirror is 6 or 8 times the mirror's diameter. But the best telescopes for observing the planets are of long focus, about f/12—the

Phases of an inferior planet: Diagram shows why Venus and Mercury are brightest when in crescent phase. (Compare with photos on page 61.) Apparent size of crescent is greater than that of full disk.

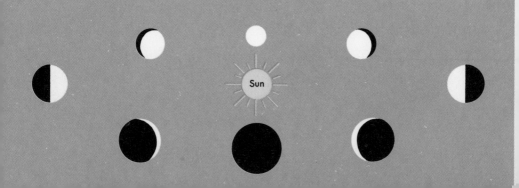

	Saturn	Uranus	Neptune	Pluto
	9.539	19.182	30.058	39.518
	886.14	1,782.80	2,793.50	3,670.00
	744 to 1,028	1,606 to 1,960	2,677 to 2,910	2,670 to 4,700
	71,500	29,500	26,800	3,600
	29.46 yrs.	84.0 yrs.	164.8 yrs.	248.4 yrs.
	$10^h02^m\pm$	$10.8^h\pm$	$15.8^h\pm$	6.4^d
	18.5	3.8	2.5	–
	9	5	2	?
	2	0	0	0
	5	0	0	0
	−0.4 to +0.9	+5.7	+7.6	+14
	yellow†	green	yellow	yellow

ratio of many refractors. The long focus cuts down the field of view but increases magnification. Experiment with your equipment to determine the magnification that will give the best results.

Mercury and Venus

Mercury, the smallest planet, is apparently a bleak and airless ball of rock, scorched on one side and frozen on the other. Being so near the Sun, it is almost always hidden in the glare. However, several times a year, near elongation, it is visible just after sunset (as evening star) or just before sunrise (as morning star).

Mercury's magnitude varies from about −1.9 to +1.1. Times when it can be seen are indicated in most almanacs and sometimes in newspapers. Many people have never seen it, but actually it is easy to see if one looks at the right time at the right place.

Like the Moon, Mercury goes through phases that are visible in a small telescope. Some astronomers claim to have seen, also, permanent markings on the surface that resemble the markings on the Moon when viewed without optical aid.

Very interesting to watch is a passage of Mercury across the Sun's disk—the phenomenon known as a "transit." It occurs about 13 times in 100 years. The next transits will be on May 9, 1970, and Nov. 11, 1973.

Inferior planet as "morning star" and as "evening star": Phenomenon is due to relative positions of Sun, Earth, and inferior planet. Superior planets also may be called "morning" or "evening stars."

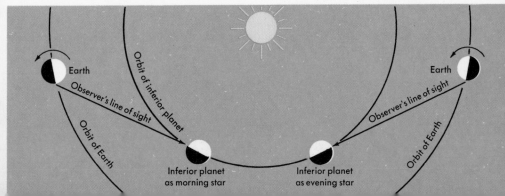

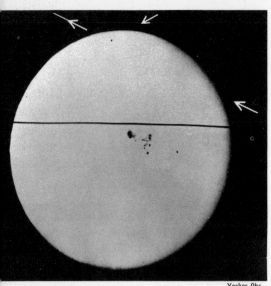

Yerkes Obs.

Transit of Mercury: Arrows at left and right indicate direction of transit, Nov. 14, 1907.

Mercury looks like a small black ball rolling slowly across the Sun's surface. (CAUTION: When observing a transit, protect the eyes! See page 49.)

Venus, nearly a twin of Earth in size, goes through phases as do our Moon and Mercury. When Venus is brightest, about magnitude −4 (it varies from −4.4 to −3.3), your telescope or binoculars will show it to be a thin crescent. When it is faintest, the entire disk is lighted. This peculiarity is due to the fact that the thin crescent phase occurs when Venus is nearest

Earth, and the full phase when it is farthest away.

Venus is the brightest planet and is sometimes visible in the daytime. Also, Venus crosses the Sun's disk as does Mercury, but this happens rarely. The last transit was in 1882; the next one will be in the year 2004.

The best time to observe Venus is in the twilight or just before dawn. Few if any permanent markings can be seen on it, because it is always shrouded in dense clouds.

Mars

The red color of Mars and its brightness (magnitude −2.8 to +1.6) make it easy to recognize. It has excited the imagination more than any other planet. Some causes of all the controversy can be seen with a small telescope: the white patches at the top and bottom of the disk, and large shaded areas on the surface.

Unfortunately the features that have stimulated greatest interest cannot be seen in very small telescopes—at least a 6-inch reflector or 3-inch refractor is necessary. Also little can be seen on Mars except when it is near Earth. Then large telescopes show distinct markings that to this day remain unexplained.

Seasons on Mars (left): As polar cap shrinks with coming of summer, brownish areas turn green.

Rotation of Mars: Red planet's day is 24h 37m—slightly longer than Earth's. Thus a feature takes little over 12 hours to move from one side of disk to other. During a few hours, markings on disk appear to change considerably.

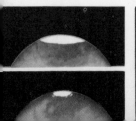

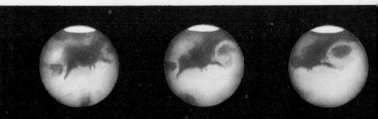

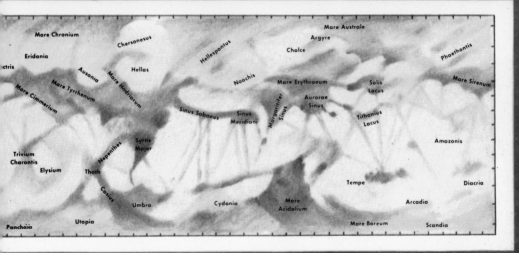

Face of Mars: As planet rotates, various features come into view. Under good conditions, most can be seen with first-rate amateur equipment. Map exaggerates features at top and bottom. (After Antoniadi)

Dark and light areas are permanent features, but some appear to change seasonally. Temporary markings that look like clouds have been observed from time to time. Some observers refer to them as "dust storms."

Other interesting areas are the so-called dark regions, of a grayish or greenish shade. These vary, but the reddish areas show little or no change.

In contrast are the white "polar caps." These show great changes that suggest seasonal effects. Sometimes a cap extends halfway to the equator, then shrinks to a small patch resembling a skull cap. The caps seem to vary according to the Martian seasons; that is, a cap is largest in the hemisphere having winter, and smallest in the one having summer. These phenomena may be true polar caps of snow.

Are there canals on Mars? Some observers see them; others do not.

However, regardless of that controversy, many fine details *are* visible. Some observers, such as members of the Association of Lunar and Planetary Observers, make detailed drawings of the planet (see pages 92-94).

The difficulty of observing minute details and small changes can be better understood when you realize that the image of the planet at the focus of a 40-inch refractor is only about 1/10 inch, or 2.5 millimeters, in diameter!

Mars drawing: Professionals and amateurs alike attempt to draw the features which they see fleetingly but which may not appear in photographs.

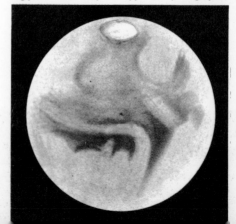

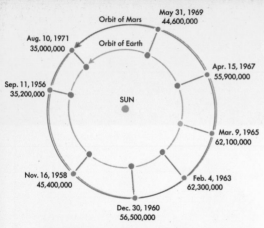

Oppositions of Mars: About every two years, orbit of Earth brings it to position between Sun and Mars. This is when Mars can be best observed. Diagram shows all oppositions from 1956 to 1971, with distance of Mars from Earth at each opposition.

Mars often is observed through filters, such as red, yellow, green, or blue. With a red filter the polar caps are not so bright, and the dark areas are darker. The opposite effect is apparent when a green or blue filter is used.

Whatever the features of Mars may be, however they can be explained, constant observation is exciting. The best power to use is about 200 with a 3-inch refractor, or somewhat higher power with a 6-inch reflector.

Asteroids

Asteroids are small planets whose orbits mostly lie between Mars and Jupiter. Some travel within the orbit of Mars and come nearer Earth than any large planets. Eros comes as near as 13.5 million miles, as it did in 1931. It will come as near again in 1975.

More than 1,500 asteroids have been discovered. Only a few hold any interest for the sky observer, and we must know exactly where to look if we want to see them. Asteroids are not confined to the zodiacal pathway; therefore amateurs often mistake them for novas (pages 86-87). The position of an asteroid, however, will be seen to change over a period of a few evenings, while the position of a nova remains the same.

Asteroids vary greatly in size—from a few miles to several hundred miles in diameter. Probably they are of irregular shapes, but no special features are visible even on the largest.

Four asteroids—Ceres, Pallas, Juno, and Vesta—are listed in the *American Ephemeris and Nautical Almanac,* which gives for each the right ascension and declination, distance from Earth, meridian transit time, and approximate magnitude for every day in the year. The positions of Eros are given only when it is most favorably situated for observing, for it is only 5 miles in diameter.

To locate an asteroid, look up its position in the *Ephemeris* and check

Transit of satellite across Jupiter's disk: In first two phases, satellite (white object) can be seen as well as its shadow. In last two phases satellite is invisible against clouds of planet. Transit takes few hours.

Dance of the moons: Four large satellites make constantly changing patterns as they revolve about Jupiter.

this position in your atlas with respect to easily identified nearby stars. You should then have little trouble finding the asteroid with telescope or binoculars.

Ceres, the first asteroid discovered, is the largest, having a diameter of about 480 miles. Pallas is the second largest, with a diameter of about 300 miles. Juno is about 115 miles, and Vesta about 230 miles, in diameter.

The brightness of asteroids depends on size, distance from Sun and from Earth, and angle of reflection of sunlight. Check magnitudes of asteroids in current *American Ephemeris*.

Jupiter

Jupiter, the largest planet, is probably a great ball of ice with a core of rock or iron. It is wrapped always in clouds of the poisonous gases methane and ammonia. This planet is one of the sky's bright objects, its magnitude varying from about −2.5 to about −1.4.

Giant Jupiter has 12 satellites, four of which are very conspicuous in a small telescope and can be seen with binoculars, their magnitude being about 6. Two of the other satellites require the power of a 12-inch tele-

Jovian portrait: Jupiter appears as photographed by large telescope. Small, bright object is satellite Ganymede; its shadow also is visible. Note planet's equatorial bulge, which is noticeable in a small telescope.

Mt. Wilson and Palomar Obs.

scope. The remaining six must be left to our largest telescopes.

The four brightest satellites, named Io, Europa, Ganymede, and Callisto, were discovered by Galileo. These hold great interest for the sky observer. Their configurations—that is, changing relative positions—throughout the year are published annually in the *American Ephemeris and Nautical Almanac* and other astronomical handbooks (see page 113).

One interesting sight is the shadow of a satellite crossing the planet's disk. Another is the cloud-like structures, or "bands," across the middle of the disk. These show changes in color and extent. Among them, and visible in a small telescope, is the so-called Red Spot—still unexplained.

Eclipses and occultations of the satellites, also, make good observing. In fact, during periods when the planet is well placed for observation, it is a rare night when some interesting Jovian phenomenon cannot be witnessed. With its sheer beauty and ever-moving moons, Jupiter is one of the most satisfying of all objects for small telescopes.

Saturn

The second-largest planet, Saturn, is a giant ball of ice wrapped in frozen clouds much like Jupiter's. It varies in magnitude from about −0.4 to about +0.9. When it is near opposition, its steady yellow light makes it a commanding object in the sky, and it vies with Jupiter for first place in beauty and interest. The rings make this planet one of the most spectacular celestial sights.

In addition to the rings, Saturn is well endowed with moons—nine of them. Like Jupiter's larger moons, Saturn's bear personal names. Those within the range of medium-size telescopes are Titan (the largest), Iapetus, Rhea, Tethys, and Dione. However, these satellites are not as active, nor do they hold as much interest, as those of Jupiter. Titan, magnitude 8, can be seen easily in small telescopes.

Of special interest is Saturn's ring system, consisting perhaps of small bits of ice. This can be seen with a telescope as small as a 1½-inch, with relatively low power. For a really good view, at least a 2½- to 4-inch refractor or a 6-inch reflector should be used. Here is one case where "the bigger, the better" holds true. With a good telescope and high power, we can see that the apparent solid band

Rings of Saturn: Details are as seen and painted, in much enlarged form, by artist after observing.

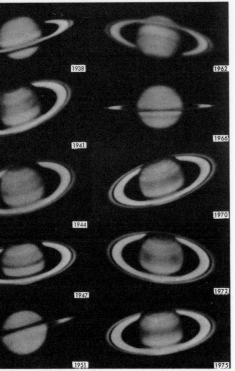

Attitudes of Saturn: Series of photos shows how planet appears to our line of sight over the years.

Uranus, Neptune, and Pluto

Uranus, the third-largest planet, is another gigantic ball of gas and ice. Its magnitude is about +6. At brightest it can be seen in binoculars. It is so far away that it takes about 84 Earth years to complete its journey around the Sun. Uranus has five moons, none of which can be seen in small telescopes.

This planet lacks any visible surface features; it is so inconspicuous that few sky observers ever see it. However, it is worth locating. Get its position from the *American Ephemeris* and plot its location on a star chart. With high power its appearance will be that of a very small, pale greenish disk.

Neptune is not much smaller than Uranus, but is much farther away. Its magnitude is about +8. Its journey around the Sun is long, requiring

is divided into two rings separated by a dark line. This dark line, discovered by the Italian astronomer J. D. Cassini in 1675, is called Cassini's Division. In large telescopes still another division has been seen in the outer of the two rings.

A peculiarity of the rings is that over a period of years we can see first one side, then the other, as the planet's tilt changes. At times the rings are edge-on and difficult to see in small telescopes, as was true in 1951. The cycle repeats after each 29½ years.

Saturn in small telescope: At 200 to 300x, planet is still small, but details may be more distinct in good instrument than can be shown here.

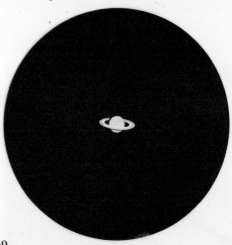

about 165 Earth years. It can be seen in good binoculars, but to spot it we must know its exact position. This can be obtained from the *Ephemeris*.

The discovery of Neptune, in 1846, was a triumph for mathematical astronomy. Its presence in a certain area of the sky was predicted before it was actually discovered. Since that time it has traveled only a little more than halfway around the Sun.

Neptune's two moons are too faint to be seen except in very large telescopes. This planet presents nothing of interest to the sky observer except the fun of hunting for it.

Pluto is the planet farthest from the Sun, and the most recently dis-

covered. Very little is known about it.

Its discovery was another triumph for mathematical astronomy. Dr. Percival Lowell, of Lowell Observatory at Flagstaff, Arizona, made the calculations, and a young astronomer named Clyde Tombaugh discovered the planet in 1930 by comparing photographs of the same field of sky taken at different times.

Pluto's mean distance from the Sun is about 3,670 million miles, or about 40 astronomical units. It is a very faint object—14th magnitude. A 12-inch telescope may be required to see it. This small planet, probably about 3,600 miles in diameter, holds little interest for amateurs.

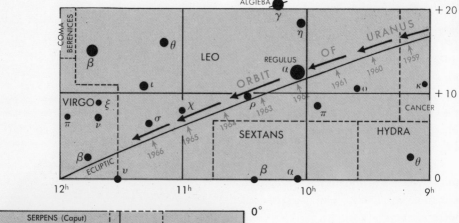

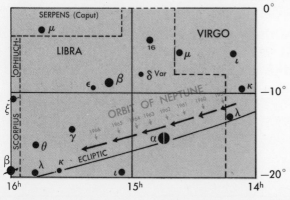

Paths of Uranus and Neptune: Maps show positions during period 1959-1966. Larger, more detailed maps would show both forward and retrograde movements during each year of this period.

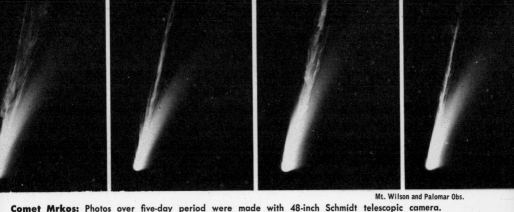

Comet Mrkos: Photos over five-day period were made with 48-inch Schmidt telescopic camera.

COMETS

The most mysterious members of the solar system are the comets. They are not regular visitors in the night sky, like planets; but they do visit us frequently—as many as five or more in a year. They usually appear suddenly, stay in view for a few weeks, then disappear. Some return after a period of years, but most do not.

One reason for the excitement of amateurs over comets is that the first person to report a *new* comet has his name given to it. No wonder many observers spend so much time seeking these elusive objects!

One of the most striking comets of many years was the eighth comet discovered in 1956. The discoverers were Arend and Roland. This was one of the few comets to exhibit a tail both fore and aft. It became so bright that it could be seen with the unaided eye despite city lights, challenging everyone to look at it. But very few comets become bright enough to be seen without binoculars or a telescope.

Comets are apparently members of our solar system. We do not know when they were made, or how, or where they come from. Apparently they shine by reflecting sunlight, as planets do; also they glow as sunlight ionizes gases in them. Comets seem to consist of gases and enormous concentrations of larger particles, perhaps meteoric material.

The tail is thought to consist of tiny particles and gases thrown off from the head. In some comets there is no tail at all, but in others it is spectacular in form and length.

Observing Pointers

Comets may appear in any part of the sky, at any time of year. Many sky observers search for comets every clear night. Instead of trying to cover the whole sky in one evening, they observe one small zone. Watching a different zone each night, they can cover much of the sky during a week.

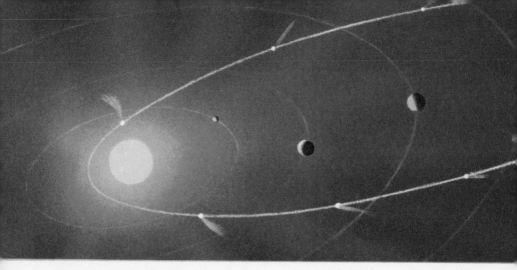

Comet's path through solar system: Unlike orbits of planets; comet's orbit is long loop. Comet tail always points away from Sun. Tail gets longer as Sun is approached, diminishes as comet moves away.

Looking for new comets or for the return of old ones—either is good sport. Many observing groups divide up the patrol work.

Binoculars can be used for comets, but a 3- to 6-inch telescope is better. Use low power to get a wide field.

Once a comet is found, a camera attached to the telescope will be useful. Because of the ability of photographic film to store up light, much more of a comet can be seen on a photograph than through the telescope. For a long-exposure photograph, some arrangement must be made to follow the comet (see page 100).

Comets change position faster than the stars. Therefore stars will show trails if the comet is clear and sharp in the photograph.

A comet can be superb in a small telescope. Usually it appears as a faint glowing object with a hazy tail. So thin is the tail that stars shine through it undimmed. The nucleus may be as small as 100 miles in diameter, or as large as 50,000 miles.

The head contains the concentrated part, called the nucleus, and the hazy material around it, called the coma. The entire head may be tremendous— 30,000 to over a million miles across.

The tail, if any, may be spectacular, spreading over a vast area. Tails generally stretch out for millions of miles; some have exceeded 100 million miles.

The tail always points away from the Sun, perhaps because of solar

SOME RECURRING COMETS		
Probable Reappearance	*Name*	*Year of Discovery*
1966 (Sep.)	Encke	1786
1966 (Oct.)	Wolff I	1884
1967 (May)	Temple II	1873
1967 (May)	Brooks II	1889
1970 (Jan.)	Pons-Winnecke	1819
1973 (May)	Arend-Roland	1956
1986	Halley	466 B.C.*

*As indicated by early records.

radiation. Tails also change in appearance from day to day. It is worth while to make frequent sketches or photographs to show these changes.

Periodic Comets

Some comets travel in elliptical orbits and, after a period of time, return again. The famous Halley's comet, last seen in 1910, probably will be seen again in 1986.

But, in general, comets are unreliable. Their periods may change, and so may their appearance. They may be bright during one visit, and faint the next. After many visits they may vanish for good. Perhaps they disintegrate, providing material for future meteor showers.

Because the return of a comet cannot be predicted with much accuracy, the observer should start hunting for it at least a month in advance. Up-to-date information about many recurring comets will be found in several current almanacs and astronomical handbooks (page 113).

On page 72 is a list of some important recurring comets, in order of the

Yerkes Obs.

Halley's Comet, May 29, 1910: Its many reappearances have made it the best-known comet.

date of probable reappearance, together with their names and dates of discovery.

Things to Do

1. Observe a zone for comets regularly.

2. Check lists of recurring comets and watch for them.

3. Plot the course of a comet on your atlas.

4. Try to predict the daily positions of a comet.

5. Make drawings or photographs to show progressive changes in a comet's appearance.

Comet study: Composite drawing was made by Comet Recorder of Association of Lunar and Planetary Observers. Reverse print shows comet details as white against dark background.

David Meisel

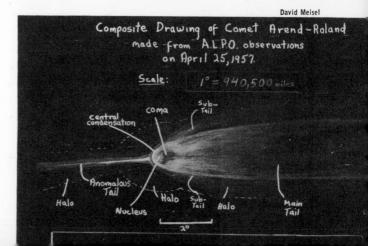

Composite Drawing of Comet Arend-Roland made from A.L.P.O. observations on April 25, 1957.

Scale: 1° = 940,500 miles

Central condensation — Coma — Sub-Tail

Anomalous Tail — Halo — Nucleus — Halo — Sub-Tail — Halo — Main Tail

2°

End of a bolide: Fast-moving stony-type meteor breaks up with a flare and a bang.

METEORS

During almost any clear night we see bright, needle-like streaks cutting across the sky—some short and some long; some bright and others faint. One, two, a dozen or more, will be seen in an hour.

People often call the objects that make these trails "shooting stars." Really they are bits of matter, stone and iron, from outer space: meteors. They race into our atmosphere with such speed—up to 44 miles per second—that friction with the air heats them to incandescence. Most turn to vapor and dust long before they can reach the ground.

Unusually slow, bright meteors are called "fireballs." Frequently their trail remains visible for some time. Fireballs that explode are "bolides."

Most meteors become incandescent 50 to 75 miles up. Some are large enough to withstand their fiery trip through our atmosphere, and fragments—from small grains to chunks as big as your fist—hit the Earth. Once in centuries a really big one arrives, such as the meteor that made Meteor Crater in Arizona.

Some meteor trails are short, and some are long —20° or more. Some are faint, others bright. They vary in color, although most are white, blue, or yellow. Some meteors are slow-moving, others very fast.

Fireballs and bolides are very bright. Their streak is thicker, lacking the usual thin, needle-like appearance. Sometimes their path is crooked or broken. Several explosions may mark their course.

74

Meteorites

Astronomers think the amount of meteoric material entering Earth's atmosphere daily may total several thousand tons. The number of meteors actually reaching the ground may be in the billions, but these are so small that their total weight is estimated at only one ton.

Fragments of meteors found on the ground are called "meteorites." From them our knowledge of the composition of meteors is obtained.

Meteorites usually have peculiar shapes and are heavy for their size. Most consist mainly of iron, some are predominantly stone, and still others consist of both. Cobalt and nickel, too, may be present.

Meteorites look fused, or melted, on the outside. Hence they may easily be confused with bits of slag. Observers who want to be able to identify meteorites should study specimens on display in planetariums and in museums.

Pointers for Observers

Meteors may be seen in any part of the sky at any time of night, throughout the year. Usually more are seen around midnight and in the early morning, because of Earth's rotation. Then, our part of Earth is facing forward in our journey around the Sun and it encounters more meteors, just as more raindrops are met by the windshield of a forward-moving car than by the rear window.

In group observing, each person watches one part of the sky for a time. Observers compete to see who can spot the most meteors. Binoculars are not necessary but do help; wide-field glasses are best.

Meteor trails make interesting photographs (see page 99). Also, amateurs with a short-wave radio receiver can "listen" to meteors. The set is tuned to a very weak distant station, preferably above 15 megacycles. The volume is kept down to almost nothing. When a meteor in the upper atmosphere ionizes a patch of air, creating a momentary "reflector" for signals, the volume of the station's signal rises sharply. Doppler changes in pitch may be heard. On a good morning, several hundred meteors may be detected.

Intruder among the stars: Brilliant meteor was caught on this 40-minute exposure of Cassiopeia region. Andromeda nebula appears near bottom.
Walter Palmstörfer, Pettenbach, Oberösterreich, Austria

PROMINENT METEOR SHOWERS

Listed here are a few of the more prominent "trustworthy" showers. Many more are listed in textbooks and handbooks.

Name	Constellation	Approx. Date	Approx. Duration (days)	Approx. No. per Hour	Radiant Point RA	Dec
Lyrids.........	Lyra	Apr. 21	4	8	18^h04^m	$+33°$
Perseids......	Perseus	Aug. 11	25	70	3^h00^m	$+57°$
Orionids.....	Orion	Oct. 19	14	20	6^h08^m	$+15°$
Leonids.......	Leo	Nov. 15	7	20	10^h00^m	$+22°$

Meteor Showers

In certain parts of the sky, at certain times of year, for a few days or weeks, greater numbers of meteors can be seen. Such concentrations are called "showers." In an hour 150 meteors may be observed. Showers occur whenever Earth, in its journey around the Sun, encounters a vast swarm of meteoric particles.

Such swarms may be the remains of comets. Some comets return several times; then, when due again, they are not seen, but brilliant showers of meteors appear where the comets were expected.

A shower appears to radiate from one point in the sky, and is likely to recur there about the same time each year. Showers are named after the constellations, or points in the constellations, from which they seem to radiate.

Things to Do

1. Observe showers, either alone or with groups.

2. Count the number of meteors seen in an hour. If observing a shower, count the number per minute.

3. On a star chart, plot point of beginning and end of meteor trails.

4. Photograph showers (page 99).

5. If a meteor falls in your vicinity, try to find it. Watch your local newspaper for reports. Find persons who saw the meteor fall and attempt to trace it. Cooperate with a nearby observatory, if any.

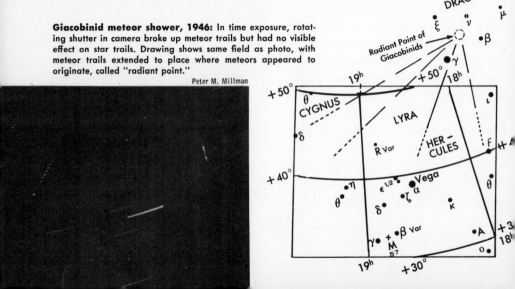

Giacobinid meteor shower, 1946: In time exposure, rotating shutter in camera broke up meteor trails but had no visible effect on star trails. Drawing shows same field as photo, with meteor trails extended to place where meteors appeared to originate, called "radiant point."

Peter M. Millman

Omega Centauri: As counterpart to northern hemisphere's Hercules cluster, southern hemisphere has this splendid aggregation of stars—a globular cluster—in Centaurus. It is visible to the unaided eye.

STARS

The galaxies — the millions of island universes in space—are made up of stars, planets and smaller bodies, gas, and dust. All the stars are spheres of glowing gas; many are millions of miles in diameter. Some are 10,000 times as thin as Earth's air at sea level, and some are so dense that a cupful of their substance would weigh tons on Earth. Star interiors have temperatures measured in millions of degrees, and at their surfaces temperatures up to 55,000°F. are common. Probably many, if not most, stars are ringed by planets.

All stars that we can see with small telescopes are within our own galaxy. The nearest one to Earth is 4½ light years away, or about 26 trillion miles. Even this nearest star, Alpha Centauri, like stars farther out, is so far distant that in the greatest telescopes with maximum magnification it is a mere point of light.

Stars differ in brightness, color, and size. Unlike the planets, they shine by their own light and, year after year, appear to remain in the same relative positions. These are the so-called "fixed" stars.

The Constellations

In ancient Greece and Rome, people noticed that the stars seemed to form figures. Legends of mythical kings and queens, of hunters and strange animals, were told about them. During the thousands of years since then, the exact star patterns have changed somewhat, but the names and legends linger. Even the professional astronomer, mapping the sky, still uses approximately the old group outlines and calls them by the old names—Cepheus the King, Cassiopeia the Queen, and Draco the Dragon. In the southern hemisphere, too, where the star groups were named much later by seafarers, names still hold —Tucana the Toucan, and Ara the Altar.

Cascade of stars: Double cluster in Perseus is fine spectacle in northern heavens. "Crosses" on brighter stars are due to optical effects in telescope.
Lick Obs.

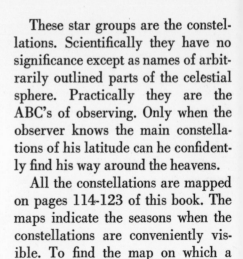

These star groups are the constellations. Scientifically they have no significance except as names of arbitrarily outlined parts of the celestial sphere. Practically they are the ABC's of observing. Only when the observer knows the main constellations of his latitude can he confidently find his way around the heavens.

All the constellations are mapped on pages 114-123 of this book. The maps indicate the seasons when the constellations are conveniently visible. To find the map on which a constellation appears, look up the constellation in the index.

Myriad Suns

Pick out any small group of stars. Look at them with the naked eye, then through binoculars, and then through a telescope with an objective of 3 inches or more. With the binoculars, and then with the telescope, you notice an almost unbelievable increase in the number of stars that are visible. And the stars themselves look different, too.

A star that to the eye looks single may appear double or even quadruple in the telescope. A small hazy patch of light may turn out to be a cluster of hundreds of stars.

Certain stars, if watched from night to night, will show changes in brightness. These are called variables. There are, also, stars that appear and vanish; they are novas, or "new stars."

The richest star fields are in the Milky Way. On a clear, dark night, far from city lights, parts of the Milky Way look like clouds. This seeming concentration of stars is due to perspective. Our galaxy, some 80,000 light years in diameter, is shaped like a double convex lens, thin at the edges and thicker toward the middle. Our solar system is about 30,000 light years from the center. When the observer on Earth looks toward the Milky Way he is looking through the galaxy toward an edge.

Almost any part of the sky makes good observing. The stars themselves present a colorful picture, from blue-white Vega and Sirius to yellow Capella and red Arcturus and Antares. See how many colors you can detect. Some of the double stars are particularly interesting because of the strong contrast in their colors—for example, Albireo (β Cygni), one of the finest doubles.

Point your telescope or binoculars to any part of the Milky Way, particularly the neighborhood of Sagittarius, toward the center of our galaxy. The myriad stars!

In star atlases many variable stars and clusters are marked. These are worth finding, and many are found easily. For certain variable stars, detailed charts are needed, or sets of coordinates so that you can plot these stars in your atlas. Detailed lists of stars with their characteristics and positions are given in textbooks, as-

THE 25 BRIGHTEST STARS*
(Positions are indicated on the maps, pages 114-123)

Designation	Name	Magnitude	Distance (light years)
α Canis Majoris	Sirius	−1.4	9
α Carinae	Canopus	−0.7	98
α Centauri	(Alpha Centauri)	−0.3	4½
α Boötis	Arcturus	−0.1	36
α Lyrae	Vega	0.0	26
α Aurigae	Capella	+0.1	45
β Orionis	Rigel	+0.2	900
α Canis Minoris	Procyon	+0.4	11
α Eridani	Achernar	+0.5	118
β Centauri	(Beta Centauri)	+0.7	490
α Orionis	Betelgeuse	+0.7	520
α Aquilae	Altair	+0.8	16
α Tauri	Aldebaran	+0.8	68
α Crucis	(Alpha Crucis)	+0.9	370
α Scorpii	Antares	+1.0	520
α Virginis	Spica	+1.0	220
α Piscis Austrini	Fomalhaut	+1.2	23
β Geminorum	Pollux	+1.2	35
α Cygni	Deneb	+1.3	1600
β Crucis	(Beta Crucis)	+1.3	490
α Leonis	Regulus	+1.4	84
ε Canis Majoris	Adhara	+1.5	680
α Geminorum	Castor	+1.6	45
λ Scorpii	Shaula	+1.6	310
γ Orionis	Bellatrix	+1.6	470

*From *The Observer's Handbook*, Royal Astronomical Society of Canada, Toronto.

tronomical handbooks, and other publications (see page 113).

In many star atlases, certain objects are labeled "M," with a number following. The M refers to the list of clusters and nebulas prepared by the old-time French astronomer Charles Messier. The list includes about 100 interesting objects visible in small telescopes. If your atlas does not show them, refer to a list of Messier objects and plot them in your atlas. Then see how many you can locate.

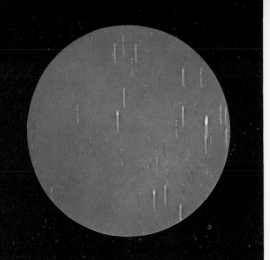

Univ. of Michigan Obs.

Star spectra: For this color photo of Hyades, an open cluster, prism was used to break up light of stars into the separate colors. (Background color is due to photographic process employed.)

Star Observing Tips

Binoculars will help you to view stars and clusters, but the low power is severely limiting. A 3- to 6-inch refractor, or a 6- to 12-inch reflector, is far better. Preferably it should be an equatorial with setting circles, so that when properly oriented it can be trained on faint objects easily.

The so-called rich-field telescope, a type of instrument with short focus and a very wide field, provides fine views of clusters and nebulas.

The best time to observe the stars and star clusters is when the atmosphere is still and clear. The longest period of good observing over the entire sky is between last quarter and first quarter of the Moon. As the Moon nears full, observe that part of the sky farthest from it.

Observe double stars when the "seeing" is especially good; that is, when the stars look like steady points of light and do not twinkle much. All stars are best observed when well above the horizon.

When at the telescope, keep both eyes open, to relieve strain. Learn to make the most of a quick glance. If the observing eye tires, close it for a moment now and then to rest it, and then open it *at* the eyepiece.

If you have a refractor, observe with the dew cap on. This helps to keep out extraneous light and darken the background, so that faint objects can be seen better. A faint object that is stared at for very long may seem to become fainter, because of eye fatigue.

Use averted vision. Look a little to the side of the object, and it will be brighter and clearer.

Multiple Stars

Most of the stars called "multiple" are either double, triple, or quadruple. The next to the last star in the handle of the Big Dipper is a visual double star, easily seen as such. The brighter of the two is named Mizar, and its fainter nearby companion is Alcor. They rotate about a common center. In a telescope, Mizar also can be seen as a double.

Epsilon (ϵ) Lyrae is a good test for eyesight, for it can be seen with the unaided eyes as a very close double near the limit of visibility. It is easily "split," or seen as a double, with a pair of binoculars. Also, each of the two stars seen in binoculars can be split with a small telescope, using a power of from 100 to 200. Epsilon Lyrae is a quadruple star, or as it is frequently called, a "double double." Polaris (North Star) and Castor (α Geminorum) are doubles. Each can be split with a 3-inch.

Besides being beautiful to look at, double stars can be used to test the optics of your instrument (see pages 16-17).

SOME INTERESTING DOUBLE STARS

Constellation	Star	Magni-tudes	Distance Apart (sec.)	Colors	Position (1950) RA	Dec
Andromeda	γ	3.0, 5.0	10	yellow, blue	02ʰ00ᵐ	+42.1°
Aquarius	ζ	4.4, 4.6	3	white, white	22ʰ26ᵐ	−00.3°
Boötes	ε	3.0, 6.3	3	orange, green	14ʰ43ᵐ	+27.3°
Cancer	ι	4.4, 6.5	30	yellow, blue	08ʰ44ᵐ	+29.0°
Canes Venatici	α	3.2, 5.7	20	blue, blue	12ʰ54ᵐ	+38.6°
Capricornus	α¹, α²	4.0, 3.8	376	yellow, yellow	20ʰ15ᵐ	−12.7°
Cassiopeia	ι	4.2, 7.1, 8.1	2, 7	yellow, blue, blue	02ʰ25ᵐ	+67.2°
Centaurus	α	0.3, 1.7	4	yellow, red	14ʰ37ᵐ	−60.6°
Corona Borealis	ζ	4.1, 5.0	6	white, blue	15ʰ38ᵐ	+36.8°
Crux	α	1.4, 1.9	5	blue, blue	12ʰ24ᵐ	−63.8°
Cygnus	β	3.0, 5.3	35	yellow, blue	19ʰ29ᵐ	+27.8°
Delphinus	γ	4.0, 5.0	10	yellow, green	20ʰ44ᵐ	+16.0°
Draco	ν	4.6, 4.6	62	white, white	17ʰ31ᵐ	+55.2°
Draco	ψ	4.0, 5.2	31	yellow, purple	17ʰ43ᵐ	+72.2°
Eridanus	32	4.0, 6.0	7	yellow, blue	03ʰ52ᵐ	−03.1°
Gemini	α	2.7, 3.7	5	white, white	07ʰ31ᵐ	+32.0°
Hercules	α	3.0, 6.1	4	orange, green	17ʰ12ᵐ	+14.4°
Lyra	ε	4.6, 4.9	208	yellow, blue	18ʰ43ᵐ	+39.6°
Lyra	ε¹	4.6, 6.3	3	yellow	18ʰ43ᵐ	+39.6°
Lyra	ε²	4.9, 5.2	2	blue	18ʰ43ᵐ	+39.6°
Orion	β	1.0, 8.0	9	blue, blue	05ʰ12ᵐ	−08.2°
Orion	θ in M42	4.0, 10.3, 2.5, 6.3	(Quad-ruple)	blues	05ʰ36ᵐ	−02.6°
Perseus	η	4.0, 8.5	28	yellow, blue	02ʰ47ᵐ	+55.7°
Scorpius	α	1.2, 6.5	3	red, white	16ʰ26ᵐ	−26.3°
Triangulum	ι or 6	5.0, 6.4	4	yellow, blue	02ʰ10ᵐ	+30.1°
Tucana	β	4.5, 4.5	26	blue, white	00ʰ29ᵐ	−63.2°
Ursa Major	ζ	2.4, 4.0	14	white, white	13ʰ22ᵐ	+55.2°
Ursa Minor	α	2.5, 8.8	19	yellow, blue	01ʰ49ᵐ	+89.0°
Virgo	γ	3.6, 3.7	6	white, yellow	12ʰ39ᵐ	−01.2°

Albireo in binoculars: Object appears as single star (large star near center of field).

Albireo in telescope: Star appears as double. Magnification reduces field.

Epsilon Lyrae in binoculars: Object appears as ordinary double in starry field.

Epsilon Lyrae in telescope: At 100x or more, double becomes pair of doubles in dark field.

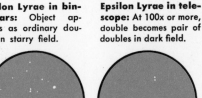

Star Clusters

Star clusters are groups of stars that travel together through space. "Open" clusters are those in which the stars are widely separated and can be resolved easily in small telescopes. "Globular" clusters are those in which the stars are closely crowded toward the center. In some globulars the individual stars cannot be resolved in a small telescope; the cluster is just a little hazy spot.

Most clusters are a treat to see. These "star sprays" glint and sparkle in a way no photograph could suggest.

The Pleiades (or "Seven Sisters") form what might be called a visual open cluster—easy for the unaided eye. In a small telescope, they are seen to number hundreds. In a large telescope the Pleiades appear enveloped in clouds of luminous gas.

The Hyades are another fine wide cluster. Best of all is the Double Cluster in Perseus.

Some clusters, at the limit of visibility for the eye, magically turn into groups of thousands of stars when the telescope is trained on them.

Beehive cluster (M44): This open group of stars, known also as the Praesepe cluster, is faint to unaided eye but makes fine show in binoculars. Look for it about 14° southeast of Pollux.

Yerkes Obs.

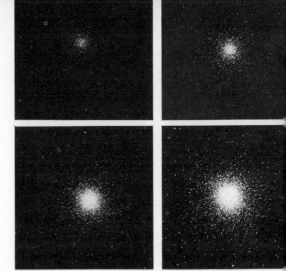

Light-gathering power: Photos of Hercules cluster M13 by 60-inch reflector with exposures of 6, 15, 37, and 95 minutes suggest appearance of M13 in telescopes of increasing power.

Look at M13—one of the best. To the eye alone it looks like a hazy star. It is easy to see as a little round cloud in binoculars. But in a 4-inch telescope you begin to resolve the stars. This globular may have 100,000!

Contrast M13 with M44, a beautiful open cluster. In this, our large telescopes can detect about 400 stars.

Mt. Wilson and Palomar Obs.

A FEW FAMOUS STAR CLUSTERS

M—Messier's list   NGC—Dreyer's *New General Catalogue*   △—Dunlop's catalogs

Constellation	Object	RA	Dec	Type	Remarks
		Position (1950)			
Auriga	M38	05h25m	+35.8°	Open	Cruciform
Auriga	M37	05h49m	+32.6°	Open	Fine open cluster
Cancer	M44	08h37m	+20.2°	Open	{ "Praesepe" (Beehive) ; Visible to eye
Canes Venatici	M3	13h40m	+28.6°	Globular	{ Separable with 4- to 6-in. telescopes
Cassiopeia	M103	01h30m	+60.4°	Open	Good field with red star
Centaurus	NGC 3766 or △289	11h34m	−61.3°	Open	Fine in binoculars
Centaurus	ω	13h24m	−47.0°	Globular	Spectacular; visible to eye
Crux	NGC 4755 or △301	12h51m	−60.1°	Open	{ Colorful cluster around κ (red star)
Cygnus	M39	21h30m	+48.2°	Open	Bright; large
Gemini	M35	06h06m	+24.4°	Open	Use binoculars
Hercules	M13	16h40m	+36.6°	Globular	{ "Great Cluster"; some resolution in 6-in.
Lacerta	75	22h13m	+49.6°	Open	Good field
Pegasus	M15	21h28m	+12.0°	Globular	Bright
Perseus	NGC 869 and 884	02h18m	+56.9°	Open	{ Double cluster; red star in center of 884
Perseus	M34	02h39m	+42.5°	Open	Large field; visible to eye
Sagittarius	M23	17h54m	−19.0°	Open	Use telescope; low power
Scorpius	M6	17h37m	−32.2°	Open	Like butterfly wing
Scorpius	M7	17h51m	−34.8°	Open	Bright; visible to eye
Scutum	M11	18h48m	−06.3°	Open	Bright
Taurus	M45	03h44m	+24.0°	Open	"Pleiades"; visible to eye
Triangulum Australe	NGC 6025 or △304	15h59m	−60.4°	Open	Bright
Tucana	NGC 104 or △18	00h22m	−72.4°	Globular	"47 Tucanae"; visible to eye

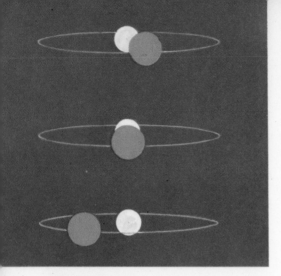

Why Algol "winks": When one of its two components passes in front of the other, light of Algol as we see it is dimmed. Complete cycle takes 2¾ days.

Variable Stars

The light output of many stars varies. Some show a regular variation in a few hours, some over a period of many days, and others over several years. Many are irregular; they have no definite period of variation.

Regular variable stars differ in the amount they vary and in the lengths of their periods, but their behavior is fairly predictable. Irregular variables are unpredictable. They may remain at the same brightness for long periods of time before they begin to vary; or they are continually varying.

The short-period regular variables are of two kinds—eclipsing and pulsating. The best example of an eclipsing variable is Algol (β Persei), for its variation can be observed without optical aid. This star is actually a

double, with two members revolving about a common center, and the variation occurs as one member passes in front of the other—thus cutting off part of its light—at regular intervals. With Algol the eclipse occurs in about 4 hours, at intervals of about 2¾ days. At maximum Algol is at about 2.2 magnitude, and at minimum about 3.5.

Pulsating variables are single stars that contract and expand at regular

AAVSO

AAVSO chart: With this chart, variable star observer estimates brightness of Omicron Ceti (small dot in circle, low right center) by reference to magnitudes of nearby stars that do not vary in brightness.

SOME WELL-KNOWN VARIABLE STARS

Constellation	Variable	Harvard Designation*	Period (days)	Mag. Range Max.	Mag. Range Min.	Position (1950) RA	Position (1950) Dec	Remarks
Andromeda	R	001838	409	6.1	14.9	00h21m	+38.3°	Long period
Carina	ι	094262	36	5.0	6.0	09h44m	−62.3°	Pulsating
Cassiopeia	RZ	023969	1.2	6.4	7.8	02h44m	+69.4°	Eclipsing binary
Centaurus	T	133633	91	5.5	9.0	13h39m	−33.4°	Semi-regular
Cepheus	T	210868	390	5.4	11.0	21h09m	+68.3°	Long period
Cepheus	δ	222557	5.4	3.6	4.3	22h27m	+58.2°	Pulsating
Cetus	o	021403	332	2.0	10.1	02h17m	−03.2°	Long period ("Mira")
Corona Borealis	R	154428	−	5.8	14.8	15h46m	+28.3°	Irregular
Cygnus	χ	194632	409	3.3	14.2	19h49m	+32.8°	Long-period
Leo	R	094211	313	5.4	10.5	09h45m	+11.7°	Long period
Lepus	R	045514	433	5.9	10.5	04h57m	+14.9°	Long period ("The Crimson Star")
Lyra	β	184633	12.9	3.4	4.1	18h48m	+33.3°	Eclipsing binary
Pavo	κ	184667	9.1	4.8	5.7	18h52m	−67.3°	Pulsating
Perseus	β	030140	2.9	2.2	3.5	03h05m	+40.8°	Eclipsing binary ("Algol")
Scutum	R	184205	−	4.7	7.8	18h45m	−05.8°	Semi-regular
Triangulum	R	023133	266	5.7	12.6	02h34m	+34.0°	Long period
Virgo	R	123307	146	6.2	12.1	12h36m	+07.3°	Long period

*Designations are derived from 1900 RA (hours and minutes) and declination (degrees only). Star positions have since changed slightly. Italic numbers indicate minus declination.

intervals. Their light output increases and decreases accordingly.

The star Omicron Ceti (Mira) is one of the most famous variable stars. It rises from a faint 10th magnitude minimum to a brilliant 3rd magnitude (at times even to 2nd magnitude) in about 150 days. It takes a little longer, about 180 days, to fade again to minimum. Because of this great range in brightness, which sometimes makes it visible to the unaided eye, it has been mistaken for a nova.

Observing Variables

Observation of variables is a field of research in which the sky observer excels. Continual observations of nearly a thousand such stars are made by members of the American Association of Variable Star Observers (AAVSO), who live all over the world. Observers periodically send to headquarters their estimates of the current star magnitudes, and these estimates are used to prepare so-called light curves. Light curves of regular variables can be used to predict the approximate times of maximum and minimum brightness.

The procedure for observing a variable is essentially simple. The observer has a special chart which helps him to locate the variable. This chart shows, also, the magnitudes of

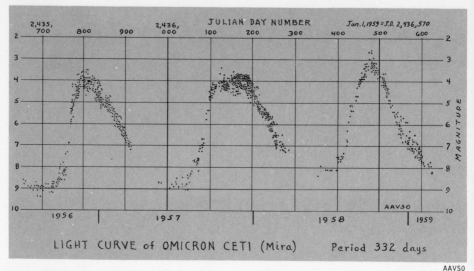

Light curve of Mira: In this chart prepared by AAVSO, each dot represents an observation.

nearby stars that do not vary in brightness. By comparing the variable with these other stars, an estimate of the variable's present brightness can be made. This estimate is recorded along with the name of the star and the time of the observation.

Some variables are easy to find and check. Others, more difficult, offer a challenge to the experienced observer with sporting blood. Red variables, for example, are deceptive; they tend to look brighter than they are. A variable that is extremely close to a much brighter star can be "tough." Some variables are members of pairs that are hard to separate even with high power. The greater the difficulty, some observers say, the greater is the sport.

Continual observation of variables by amateurs for over 50 years has helped professional astronomers toward knowledge of the structure, composition, and evolution of the universe. Data provided by the AAVSO are continually used in astronomical research.

Novas

Novas are a special class of variables. They usually rise swiftly from obscurity, then slowly fade—sometimes beyond the limits of the greatest telescopes. Some flare up again later, but most become faint variables or disappear from view entirely. It is not known exactly what makes novas, but they are undoubtedly a manifestation of an explosion of vast proportions.

One nova that "rose again" was RS Ophiuchi. It burst forth in 1898 and again in 1933. Then, in July

A FEW RECURRING NOVAS

Nova	Constellation	AAVSO Designation	Magnitude Max.	Magnitude Min.	Observed Dates of Maximum
T	Corona Borealis	155526	2.0	11.0	1866, 1946
RS	Ophiuchus	174406	4.0	11.5	1898, 1933, 1958
T	Pyxis	090031	7.0	14.0	1890, 1902, 1920, 1944
U	Scorpius	161617	8.8	Fainter than 17	1863, 1906, 1936

1958, it burst forth again and rose to a magnitude of about 5.5. An alert amateur in Maine, Cyrus Fernald, noted this new outburst and reported it promptly. Observatories at once began observing the star's spectrum.

Just as some observers sweep the sky for comets, others patrol it for novas. By organizing into groups, with each member responsible for a certain area, most of the sky can be "covered." Night after night the individual observer takes a look at his zone, in the hope of noticing an intruder. No one knows when it will happen, and the amateur sky watcher has as good a chance of making the discovery as anyone else.

Things to Do

1. Observe the Milky Way at all times of the year.

2. Try to split doubles near the limit of resolution (page 16) of your telescope.

3. Observe variables and plot their changes in brightness.

4. When a nova has been announced, observe it and make your own light curve.

5. See how many Messier objects you can find with your telescope.

6. With a star chart such as the one on page 84, test the capacity of your eyes to detect faint stars.

Nova Herculis: Photographs show star before (left) and at the time of its outburst in the year 1934.

Yerkes Obs.

Island universe: Brightest spiral galaxy visible in northern hemisphere, Andromeda nebula M31 is faint to unaided eye. It is seen as glowing spot in binoculars and telescopes. Individual stars are not resolved. Spiral structure appears only in time-exposure photos. Large spots nearby are satellite nebulas.

NEBULAS

Many objects in the sky appear in a small telescope as hazy masses. Because of their cloudy appearance they have been called nebulas (from Latin *nebula*, "mist" or "cloud"). Not until the advent of the large telescope and the astronomical camera was the nature of these nebulas discovered.

Galaxies

Many so-called nebulas can be resolved in our great telescopes and appear as enormous swarms of individual stars. Some have a spiral form; others are elliptical or relatively formless. Today these nebulas are more correctly termed "galaxies" or "island universes," for they are outside our own star system, and are great systems themselves.

The Andromeda nebula M31 can be seen without optical aid. It is like a very tiny, thin cloud. In binoculars and small telescopes it is visible as an elliptical, hazy mass—like a light held behind a dark curtain. A time-exposure photograph taken with a very large telescope shows M31 to be a pinwheel-like crowd of individual stars seen almost edge on. The Andromeda nebula is considered similar to the galaxy or universe of stars in which our own Sun and planets exist. It is about 1½ million light years distant, and measures about 120,000 light years across.

Observers in the southern hemisphere are familiar with the Magellanic Clouds. These prominent objects are island universes of irregular form, 150,000 light years distant.

Diffuse Nebulas

Within our galaxy are great clouds of gas and dust that are called "diffuse," or "galactic," nebulas. Some are dark and some are bright. Typical of the dark nebulas are those in the constellations Crux, Cepheus, Cygnus, and Scorpius. Such nebulas appear like ragged black "holes" in the sky. Actually, they hide stars beyond.

In the "sword" of Orion is the typical bright nebula M42, faint to the unaided eye but impressive in binoculars and small telescopes (see pages 9 and 95). It is about 30 light years across, and 2,000 light years distant.

Diffuse nebulas are diffuse indeed —usually less dense than the air that remains in the most "perfect" vacuum that man can make in the laboratory.

The gases and dust of diffuse nebulas may be material from which stars are even now being formed. Some such nebulas shine by reflecting the light of nearby stars. Others glow, like fluorescent lamps, as starlight strikes them.

The so-called planetary nebula, a common type, consists of gas apparently blown out by a star during catastrophic change. The gas forms an envelope or "shell" around the star. This shell may appear to us as a ring, as does the Ring Nebula in Lyra.

Diffuse nebulas within the amateur's range include the Crab Nebula in Taurus, the Great Looped Nebula in Dorado, and the Lagoon Nebula in Sagittarius.

Magellanic Clouds: These enormous clusters of stars, about 150,000 light years distant from our Milky Way Galaxy, are other "universes." They are visible to unaided eye in southern hemisphere. Bright object at upper left is the star Achernar.

Harvard Obs.

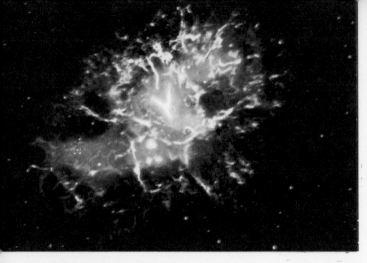

Crab Nebula (M1) in Taurus: Spectroscopic evidence indicates gases of this diffuse nebula are rushing outward at about 700 miles per second. Chinese astronomers in 11th century reported nova (exploding star) at this location. M1 is dim but well defined in small telescopes.

Messier listed as nebulas many objects which we know now are globular clusters. Modern lists of Messier objects classify these objects according to our present knowledge of them.

Pointers for Observers

Galaxies can be resolved into individual stars only by means of time-exposure photographs taken through large telescopes. Nevertheless, tele-

Planetary nebula (NGC 7293) in Aquarius: Gases from exploded star, rushing outward, form expanding shell. Ring Nebula in Lyra (M57) is similar. Many planetaries are visible to amateurs.

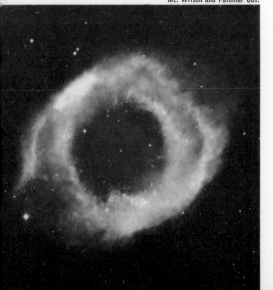

scopes of 3 to 6 inches will bring many such galaxies into view. Telescopes of 6 to 12 inches will add many more, and increase their beauty.

Most nebulas can be well observed only on clear, dark, moonless nights, away from city lights. The Magellanic Clouds and the great nebulas in Andromeda and Orion are bright enough to be observed under almost any conditions, but the darker the sky, the better.

These great nebulas are easy to locate. For others you may need an atlas. Determine the exact position of the nebula in relation to nearby bright stars; then work your way to it. With an equatorial telescope you may be able to locate the nebula by means of its coordinates.

Spirals seen broadside may look like round clouds. If tipped with respect to our line of vision, they may appear oval. If we see them edge on, a glowing mass may be visible in the middle of a double convex lens-

NOTABLE GALAXIES AND GASEOUS NEBULAS

M   Messier's list
NGC   Dreyer's *New General Catalogue*

△   Dunlop's catalogs
H   Sir William Herschel's catalog

Constellation	Object	Position (1950) RA	Dec	Type	Remarks
Andromeda	M31	00ʰ40ᵐ	+41.0°	Spiral gal.	"Great Nebula"; visible to eye
Canes Venatici	M51	13ʰ28ᵐ	+47.4°	Spiral gal.	"Whirlpool nebula"
Dorado	NGC 2070 or △142	05ʰ39ᵐ	−69.2°	Diffuse neb.	"Great Looped Nebula"; visible to eye
Draco	NGC 6543 or H37	17ʰ59ᵐ	+66.6°	Planetary neb.	Bright blue disk
Lyra	M57	18ʰ52ᵐ	+33.0°	Planetary neb.	"Ring Nebula"
Orion	M42 or θ	05ʰ33ᵐ	−05.4°	Diffuse neb.	"Great Nebula"
Perseus	M76	01ʰ39ᵐ	+51.3°	Planetary neb.	
Sagittarius	M20	17ʰ59ᵐ	−23.0°	Diffuse neb.	"Trifid Nebula"
Sagittarius	M8	18ʰ01ᵐ	−24.4°	Diffuse neb.	"Lagoon Nebula"; visible to eye
Sagittarius	M17	18ʰ18ᵐ	−16.2°	Diffuse neb.	"Omega" or "Horseshoe" nebula
Taurus	M1	05ʰ32ᵐ	+22.0°	Diffuse neb.	"Crab Nebula"
Triangulum	M33	01ʰ31ᵐ	+30.4°	Spiral gal.	Faint
Ursa Major	M81	09ʰ52ᵐ	+69.3°	Spiral gal.	"The Great Spiral"
Ursa Major	M97	11ʰ12ᵐ	+55.3°	Planetary neb.	"Owl Nebula"
Vulpecula	M27	19ʰ58ᵐ	+22.6°	Planetary neb.	"Dumbbell Nebula"

shaped structure. The apparent shape of any nebula depends on its position with relation to our line of sight.

Diffuse nebulas may appear as a luminous veil. In some there is a star surrounded by a luminous material, like a neon light in fog. Typical of these is M42 in Orion. The Crab Nebula in Taurus suggests a thin "splash" of light.

A planetary nebula, such as those in Lyra and Aquarius, may appear as a glowing cloud-like ring or wheel. The usual star in the center may or may not be visible. M27, in Vulpecula, looks elliptical.

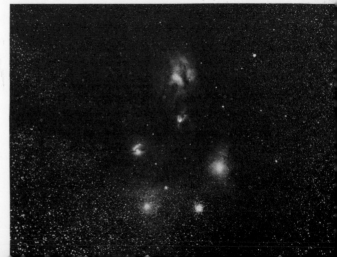

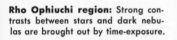
Rho Ophiuchi region: Strong contrasts between stars and dark nebulas are brought out by time-exposure.

Harvard Obs.

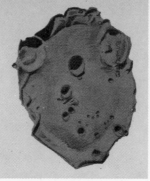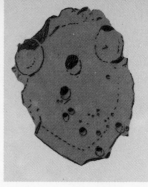

Changing Moon crater: Two drawings (left) of Clavius indicate how appearance of Moon feature will change because of Moon's librations (rocking or wobbling motions).

Rough technique: Sketch of Clavius (extreme right) suggests useful pencil technique for inexperienced artists.

DRAWING SKY OBJECTS

The drawing of sky objects does not demand great artistry, but it sharpens your perception and heightens your awareness of the variety in celestial objects. Drawings lead to interesting discussions with fellow-observers and may have scientific value.

A good 2- or 3-inch instrument can reveal enough to make drawing worth while, especially as to the Moon. An equatorial mounting with a clock drive helps because it enables you to draw without stopping frequently to re-sight the telescope.

Use of a Barlow lens (page 107) will allow you to obtain high magnification while using a comfortable low-power eyepiece.

Materials for drawing can be as simple as a pen-light, pencil, and notebook. Worth trying are 3B Wolff pencils, 2B lead pencils, charcoal, india ink, stomps, kneaded rubber, and a spiral-bound sketch book of heavy, good paper. A spray of fixative will keep a pencil drawing from smudging. A compass makes neat circles; or any round object may do.

For drawing the Moon, a street or porch light may provide enough extra illumination. For fainter objects, a small flashlight can be shielded and clamped on the sketch pad.

Moon features (see page 44) are clearest when near the terminator; then their shadows provide high contrast. Lightly indicate the over-all area and proportions; then add details. Locate details in relation to other details nearby.

Make drawings large enough—don't be cramped. For example, a good length for the Moon crater Clavius is 5 or 6 inches. Set boundaries with light pencil marks at the start.

A series of drawings of an object should be on the same scale. Then the drawings can be compared and better

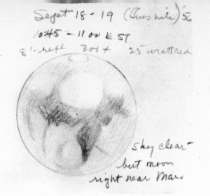
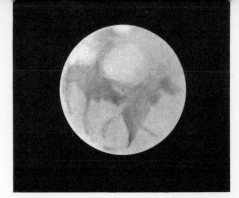

Sketch and finish: Sketch of Mars (left) was preliminary to drawing which artist finished later.

appreciated. A lunar feature may change its appearance from time to time because of the Moon's librations, or apparent tilting.

Work on a small area at one time. A Moon crater such as Copernicus will provide work for an evening.

Try for details and accuracy; let beauty take care of itself. If delicate shadings are hard to get, try the simple type of rendering shown above.

For Mars and other planets, start with a 2-inch circle. Rough in large areas first, then work on details. Include all details seen, however fleeting. Work as fast as good standards permit, because of the planet's rotation. When the essentials are done, take the drawing indoors and refine it while your impressions are fresh.

When Mars is near opposition, interesting features can be seen with a

Artist's preliminary sketch: Painting of Orion nebula, page 9, was based on this rough sketch made at telescope. Lines drawn on sketch aided artist in proper placement of stars on the finished painting.

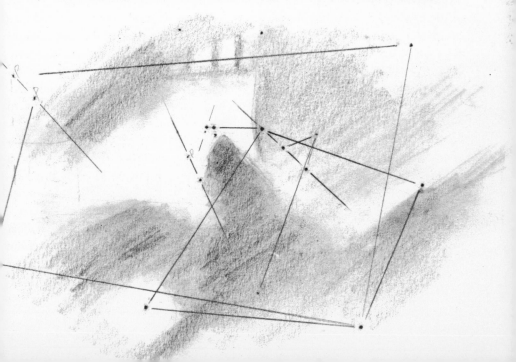

6-inch reflector. The observer discerns little at first, but the ability of the eye to make out detail improves. A polar cap may gradually appear as a lighter spot on the planet. Other broad features may be visible when seeing is good. A red filter is worth trying.

The recommended power for Mars is 200 to 300x. A 6- to 8-inch telescope is likely to be needed for even fleeting glimpses of the "canals."

Sketch the changing positions of Jupiter's larger satellites during an evening. Record the passage of a satellite's shadow across the disk. An 8-inch reflector with high power can break down some cloud belts into delicately colored festoons, red spots, and other forms. Take account of this planet's rapid rotation.

The Cassini division in Saturn's rings will appear in a 3-inch. With a 6-inch reflector, under good conditions, many faintly colored cloud bands can be distinguished, and sometimes the shadow of the globe against the rings. Also worth sketching is the changing angle of the rings.

With every drawing, record the essential data—date, hour, phase of Moon or planet, stage of rotation of planet (which meridian is at the center), longitude and latitude of feature (if your chart gives this information), seeing conditions, size of telescope, magnification used, and any peculiarities noticed — such as a "cloud" on Mars or apparent meteor hit on the Moon.

Comets present an interesting challenge. So do the filmy arms of nebulas, sunspots (caution!), auroras, and eclipse phenomena.

—John and Cathleen Polgreen

Partial lunar eclipse: Moon rises partially eclipsed, then gradually emerges from shadow of Earth as photographer makes exposures at 5-minute intervals. In foreground is Central Park, New York City.

American Museum of Natural History

THE SKY OBSERVER'S CAMERA

When viewing an object, the human eye cannot store up the light it receives. Photographic film, however, can do just that. The longer the film is exposed, the more light it stores up, and the images of fainter and fainter objects are recorded on the film. This is the main reason why professional astronomers today can probe deeper into space than astronomers of 200 years ago.

Pictures of stars, Moon, and other objects can be made with any kind of camera. Even an old box Brownie will get good results. For more striking pictures, a camera with a long-focus portrait lens or a telescopic lens is worth trying. Advanced work can be done with telescope and film holder, or telescope and camera.

The Astro-Camera

Some objects, such as planets, are mere specks in pictures taken with a camera alone. The pictures should be taken through the telescope with an astro-camera or ordinary camera.

An astro-camera, which can be bought or made at home, is essentially a light-tight box a few inches long, painted flat black inside, with a film holder at the rear. At the front it has a movable adapter tube which fits into the eyepiece holder. The telescope objective serves as the camera lens.

To find the proper position for the film holder, remove it and substitute a ground-glass holder (ground side toward objective). Adjust camera so

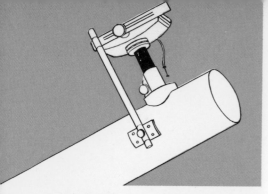

Camera holder on telescope: Devices like this are available from dealers. Some observers design and make their own.

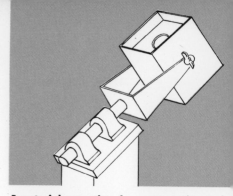

Equatorial mounting for camera: This simple type of mounting, hand- or clock-driven, can be used for camera not attached to equatorial telescope.

as to get the best obtainable image on the glass (wearing your eye glasses if you use them). Then replace the film holder.

For a larger image, use an eyepiece in the adapter. Focus with a ground glass.

If the astro-camera lacks a regular shutter, the slide that protects the film in the film holder can be used as a substitute shutter. To start the exposure, pull the slide almost all the way out. To stop it, push the slide back in. Exposures of less than a few seconds cannot be made in this way. For pictures of Sun and Moon, which require very short exposures, a shutter from an old camera can be built into the astro-camera.

A makeshift shutter can be made out of a large piece of cardboard. In this, cut a slit about ¼ or ½ inch wide, longer than the diameter of the objective. With the cardboard, mask the telescope while the slide is removed from the film holder (carefully, so as not to move the telescope tube). Then the slit is moved across the open end

of the telescope to expose the film, and the cardboard again masks the telescope while the slide is replaced.

In an astro-camera that has a lens, focus the lens as you would an eyepiece, using a ground glass.

Telescope and Camera

A camera that is used to take pictures through the telescope should be a reflex type, which can be focused by looking through the lens; or a model which uses a film holder and thus can be focused with a ground glass.

In the telescope eyepiece holder insert a low-power eyepiece and focus it as if for ordinary viewing (using your glasses if you wear them). Attach the camera to the telescope by means of some sort of camera holder (see picture above, at left). Set camera for infinity and full aperture, and focus through lens or with ground glass. To keep out extraneous light, connect eyepiece and camera lens with a sleeve of black paper.

The amateur's first efforts at photographing celestial objects through the telescope are likely to have poor success. After careful experimenting with combinations of equipment, focusing, exposure times, and other important factors, excellent results become possible.

Following the Object

While any sky picture is being taken, Earth keeps rotating. This motion makes little difference in exposures of 5 seconds or less made with camera alone, or in exposures of about ½ second or less made through the telescope. In the longer exposures needed for dim objects, these objects will blur or extend into trails unless there is a compensating motion of the camera.

With an equatorial mounting you can provide this compensating mo-

John Stofan

Star trails: Constellation Orion was photographed by letting stars trail for 2½ hours, then interrupting exposure for 5 minutes, and finally exposing film again for 30 minutes with camera "following."

How it was done: For Orion picture above, camera was mounted on equatorial telescope. In final phase, photographer watched guide star through small telescope on mounting, turning micrometer screw to keep camera on the constellation. Thus stars did not trail.

John Stofan

tion. If the picture is being taken with a camera or astro-camera attached to an equatorial telescope, the photographer can keep his instrument sighted on the object by keeping some chosen guide star centered in the finder. (This is done more easily if a high-power eyepiece is used in the finder.) If an equatorial telescope is not available, a simple mounting can be made for a camera (see picture, facing page). Such a mounting should be equipped with a finder or sights.

If the equatorial mounting has a clock drive, the observer does not need to move the tube by hand except for an occasional corrective touch. A clock drive makes exposures up to several hours practicable.

Exposures and Films

The kinds of film and plates used for sky pictures, and the proper exposures, vary widely. Follow the recommendations on the following pages for the particular purposes.

A plateholder for use with small telescopes usually takes 2¼ x 3¼ or 3¼ x 4¼ film. For 6- to 12-inch telescopes, 4 x 5 film can be used. Roll film used in cameras also is suitable.

When an eyepiece is used to enlarge the primary image, the exposure must be increased to compensate for the spreading of the light to form the larger image. If the primary image is enlarged two times, the exposure time must be multiplied by 4; and if the image is enlarged 3 times, the exposure must be multiplied by 9. That is, the exposure varies directly as the square of the number of times the primary image is magnified.

Few commercial firms do developing suitable for sky pictures. The observer should learn to do this for himself, and it is fun to do it. Hint: stick to the procedure recommended by the film manufacturer.

Star Trails

On a moonless night, load your camera with fast film. Set it on a tripod and point it at any group of bright stars. Open the diaphragm wide. Set the range at infinity. Then take a series of pictures, using 1 second, 5 seconds, 10, and so on. Next, make a time exposure of about 5 minutes. Don't advance the film during all this, but allow 1 or 2 minutes between exposures.

When the film is developed, place it over an opal glass viewer. Each star will appear on the film as a chain of images of increasing size. The longer the exposure, the longer the trails. This experiment will teach you about exposures for stars, the power in your lens, and the field of view of your camera.

Now fix the camera on a tripod. Point it at a bright star group near the equator, such as Orion. Expose

Aurora from Alaska: Northern and southern lights are a fine challenge to photographers. Opportunities occur even in temperate regions.

Steve McCutcheon

Ring Nebula in Lyra: Photo was taken through small telescope. Time exposure makes nebula more prominent than as seen in telescope.

10 minutes to an hour. In 10 minutes the stars will move 2½°; in 1 hour, 15°. The field of view of your camera can be determined by checking the length of the trails on your negative against the exposure time.

Next, point the camera toward the celestial pole. On a good clear night, expose the film for 2 or 3 hours. The apparent motion of the stars around the pole will be recorded. The trails are arcs of circles—not virtually straight lines, as in the photograph of stars near the equator.

Auroras and Meteors

For auroras any camera is useful. The 35mm cameras with fast lenses and fast films give results with short exposures. Try color as well as black and white, exposing from 1/25 second up to 30 minutes, depending on the brilliance of the aurora, aperture, and film type. For an average aurora, try 10 seconds on a film with a rating of ASA 80 or 100. Fast and panchromatic films give excellent results. Use full aperture.

The best time for photographing meteors is when a shower is due (see page 76). Keep the camera pointed a little to the side of the radiant point. Use fast and panchromatic film, exposing 10 to 30 minutes or more.

Clusters and Nebulas

For clusters and nebulas you may need the telescope—one with a good equatorial mounting and setting circles. It is possible to use a hand slow-motion drive, but a clock drive is better. Try 15 minutes and more.

With a camera alone, use fast panchromatic and high-speed films, exposing 1 hour or more for ordinary cameras. With some lenses, 30 minutes may be enough. With superfast Schmidt-type cameras, amazing results can be obtained in 10 minutes.

If the camera is guided by hand, 10 to 15 minutes is about the limit. Only the brightest of nebulas and clusters will be within your range.

The Sun

CAUTION!
When using the camera alone, place a filter over the lens, except

Jupiter in three exposures: Exposure at left caught good detail. Other disks are overexposed. Taken through 12½-inch reflector, with eyepiece.

Comet portrait: Photographer made artistic use of trees in foreground when preparing this superb 20-second exposure of Comet Arend-Roland with Speed Graphic camera.

when the Sun is in full eclipse. A gray filter is satisfactory.

During an eclipse, a filter is not necessary. Use 1/25 second at f/8 for prominences; ½ second to 3 seconds at f/8 for the inner and outer corona. Any exposure over 1 second will require guiding. (Caution!)

For the full Sun, *slow* film, *small* apertures, and *short* exposures are called for. Exposures vary, but a good guide is 1/1000 second at f/64 for the primary image on an ordinary day. This would mean an aperture of only ¾ inch for a small telescope.

For sunspots, it is best to photograph the enlarged image. Use the telescope, but put a diaphragm over the objective (see page 50) to reduce the aperture to 2 inches or less. Experiment with different apertures.

Moon, Planets, and Comets

The Moon is very bright when full; therefore slow and panchromatic film can be used as well as color. Exposures of 1/100 second to 10 seconds may be successful at f/12, depending on the phase of the Moon, your equipment, and the enlargement attempted. For a starter, try the Moon at first quarter on a fast film at 1/25 second, "shooting" through the telescope.

Mars, Jupiter, Saturn, and Venus are the most photogenic planets. Try a photograph through the telescope eyepiece, with fast and panchromatic film—5 seconds and longer. Guiding is necessary.

It is almost impossible to get a good photo of Mercury. Uranus, Neptune, Pluto, and the asteroids can be photographed like stars.

All your photos of the heavens should be carefully examined for the possible trace of a comet. Dim comets usually appear on film as a more or less shapeless faint mass.

Watch for announcements of the appearance of a comet. If it is large enough, try photographing it with your camera. Use full aperture with fast and panchromatic film, and expose 10 minutes or more. Guiding is necessary. For a small, dim comet, use the telescope.

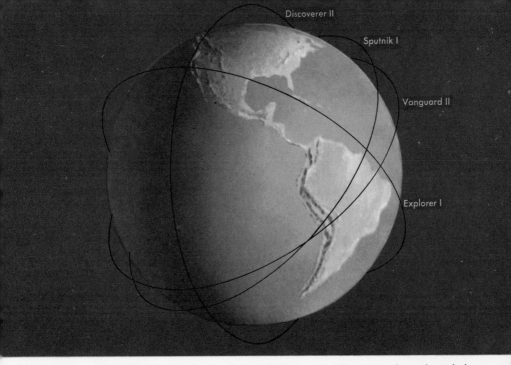

Earth satellite orbits: Orbits are like hoops, within which Earth rotates. The greater the angle made by the plane of a satellite's orbit with Earth's equator, the greater the area of Earth from which satellite can be seen. To be visible from all parts of Earth, satellite must have polar orbit.

TRACKING SATELLITES

One of the greatest scientific accomplishments of man has been the launching of artificial satellites. Manmade moons have been added to the sky, and there will be many more in years to come.

When the observer has learned his way among the stars and planets, he is able to distinguish the artificial from the natural. And he finds the observing and tracking of man-made satellites an exciting experience.

Many satellites have been launched into orbits relatively close to the earth —a few hundred miles out in space. Their speed is about 18,000 miles per hour, and they are visible from any one point for only a few minutes. Hence it is very difficult to observe them with an ordinary telescope. Wide-field and short-focus telescopes, and also high-power binoculars, are generally used. Photographing satellites is doubly difficult, but excellent pictures have been made with fast hand cameras.

Many rockets and other large objects can be easily observed without

Moonwatch team: At Fort Worth Children's Museum, Texas, whole families participated in satellite tracking.

optical help. Some of them will become artificial asteroids. Their distances from Earth and Sun will be great, their orbits large, and their motions in the sky will be slower than those of satellites that orbit between Earth and Moon.

Under the International Geophysical Year Program, sky observers in many parts of the world were organized under "Moonwatch" into small teams for tracking satellites. Accurate records of the passage of satellites over various areas were needed for checking satellite orbit predictions and for determining geographic distances, density of the atmosphere at various levels, and Earth's gravitational forces.

Moonwatch observers set to work with very simple, wide-field, 12-power telescopes. As many as a dozen instruments were set up along a north-south line, fixed so that each observer saw a different part of sky across which the satellite was likely to pass.

When an observer saw the satellite enter his field of view, he signaled to the timekeeper. Then a record was made of the exact moment when the satellite passed a check point in the field. The coordinates of this point and the time were then reported to Moonwatch headquarters. With reports coming in from Moonwatch teams all over the world, IGY scientists could keep checking the orbits and speeds of the satellites.

The "Lone-wolf" Tracker

Satellite trackers who are not on Moonwatch teams provide their own

102

equipment. Some have made or bought suitable wide-field telescopes. For the brighter satellites, binoculars can be used.

The lone satellite observer must depend mainly upon newspaper reports for information about when and where satellites and orbiting rocket stages can be seen. Usually this information is not very precise, because orbits change. The observer must "patrol" a fairly large part of the sky quickly and efficiently, within a time span of a few minutes, if he is to see the little point of light as it streaks across the sky.

From time to time, some astronomical publications (see page 113) print tables and graphs from which the observer can roughly calculate the courses of satellites in advance.

Whereas the telescope of a Moonwatch tracker remains set upon a patch of sky whose exact coordinates are known, the lone observer must keep his instrument moving. When he sees a satellite, therefore, he can determine its position only by reference to near-by bright stars whose coordinates can be looked up in his atlas.

The exact time when a satellite passes can be recorded by means of a stopwatch. The stopwatch is started at the moment when the satellite passes the check point. The observer then looks at a regular clock or watch, subtracts the time shown by the stopwatch, and thus obtains the exact time for the satellite's passage. The clock itself, of course, must be accurate.

A satellite or orbiting rocket stage of irregular shape may wobble or tumble as it moves, so that it presents a changing face to the Sun and reflects a changing amount of sunlight. Its magnitude may range from that of a bright planet to that of a star too dim for the unaided eye. Some photographs have shown this variation.

Satellites fainter than 8th or 9th magnitude may require the use of an instrument with more light-gathering area than the small tracking telescopes or binoculars offer. The larger instruments have much smaller fields, and "patroling" is difficult.

Satellite trail: Camera caught the launching rocket of first Russian satellite (1957) streaking across bowl of Big Dipper, as seen from Ottawa, Canada, Oct. 13, 1957, at 05^h 13^m 50^s E.S.T.; exposure 43 seconds.

Peter M. Millman

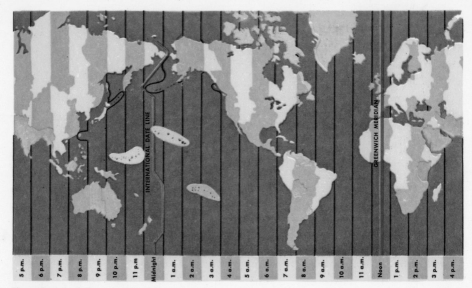

Time Zones of the World: Chart shows time in various zones when it is noon at Greenwich, England. This is Mean Time—clock time based on the average, or mean, solar day. The time at Greenwich—Greenwich Civil Time—is the so-called Universal Time which is used in astronomy and navigation.

USING ASTRONOMICAL TIME

Every sky observer should be familiar with the main principles of timekeeping. These are based on Earth's rotation and its journey around the Sun.

These motions govern our solar day, which is the interval between two successive crossings of the Sun over the same meridian. This interval varies throughout the year, because of changes in the Earth's rotation and distance from the Sun. So we use an average, or mean, solar day for everyday timekeeping.

For scientific purposes, various "kinds" of time are distinguished:

Mean Time (MT): Clock time based on the average, or mean, solar day.

Apparent Time (AT): True Sun time—not the average or mean.

Equation of Time (E): Difference between Mean Time and Apparent Time. It varies, and amounts to as much as 16 minutes.

Standard Time (ST): The Mean Time in one of the world's standard time zones. These 24 zones (one for each hour) are formed by 24 meridians (north-south lines) about 15° apart. The Standard Time in a place is the local mean time of a standard meridian near the center of the zone. ST meridians begin at 0° longitude (Greenwich, England).

Greenwich Civil Time (GCT): Local Mean Time (LMT) of 0° longitude.

Universal Time (UT): Greenwich Civil Time. Used in astronomy and navigation.

Julian Period (JP): A period devised to make it easier to calculate the exact time interval between dates. The period begins January 1, 4713 B.C. It counts the days since then regardless of changes made meanwhile in our everyday civil calendars.

Julian Day (JD): Number of the day since the beginning of JP. The Julian Day begins at noon UT and continues right through the night, measuring 24 hours consecutively, to noon UT of the next day.

Astronomical Day: Julian Day. Begins at noon UT.

Sidereal Time (ST or SidT): "Star time." Used in astronomy and navigation. Based on Sidereal Day (explanation below).

The Julian Day number for January 1, 1959, is 2,436,570; for January 1, 1960, it is 2,436,935; and so on.

The Julian Day represents a convenient way to keep observing records. If you used our everyday (Gregorian) calendar, you would write "night of January 1-2, 1960," but by using the JD number you only have to write the last 3 or 4 figures, like this: 935 or 6935.

Sidereal Time, or "Star Time," is based on the interval between two successive crossings of a star over the same meridian. This interval is the Sidereal Day, equal to about $23^h 56^m$ —about 4 minutes short of a solar day.

This 4-minute difference is due to Earth's daily progress in its journey around the Sun.

A clock that keeps Sidereal Time gains about 4 minutes a day compared with ordinary clocks. In six months it gains 12 hours, and in 12 months, 24 hours: one day.

A glance at the sidereal clock tells the astronomer the approximate location in the sky of any object of which he knows the coordinates (RA and Dec). For example, Sirius has an RA of $6^h 43^m$; so if the observer's sidereal clock shows $5^h 40^m$, Sirius is $1^h 3^m$ east of his meridian (see page 116). If the sidereal time is 14^h, Sirius is west and below the horizon. If the sidereal time is 23^h, Sirius has not risen.

The sidereal clock shows the hours from 1 to 24 hours consecutively, whereas ordinary time is read from 1 to 12 hours in two series.

The use of sidereal time and a simple method for obtaining it are explained on pages 38-39.

Comparison of clocks: Time at a given moment is shown by sidereal clock at Cambridge, Mass., and ordinary clocks at Cambridge, Mass., and Greenwich, England. Exactly 24 hours later, ordinary clocks will show same time as before, but sidereal clock will show 13h 22m—having gained 4 minutes.

13h 18m Sidereal Time Cambridge, Mass.	May 15 9:30 p.m. (2130) E.S.T. Cambridge, Mass.	May 16 2:30 a.m. (0230) Greenwich Civil Time Greenwich, England

EXTRA EQUIPMENT

Few sky observers are content to use the same old equipment year in and year out. Although there is a lifetime of pleasure in a good equatorial telescope, with its full complement of three regular eyepieces and a solar eyepiece, the observer eventually wants something more.

Mechanical Drives

A mechanical drive, one of the most useful accessories, is used on equatorial mountings. It compensates for Earth's rotation, and thus enables the observer to set the telescope on an object and keep it there.

Some observers have drives with variable speed for following Moon, comets, and planets.

A mechanical drive makes observing by oneself and with groups easier.

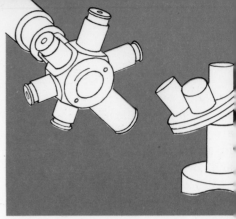

Multiple eyepiece holders: At left is holder for refractors; at right, holder for reflectors. With several eyepieces in holder, properly focused, observer can easily shift from one eyepiece to another.

It makes possible long photographic exposures, so that deep-sky wonders are brought into view.

Even with the best mechanical drive, there are small inaccuracies. Occasional hand guiding may be necessary.

Multiple Eyepieces

The multiple eyepiece, which looks like the lens turret on a home movie camera, is offered under numerous names, as turret eyepiece, Unihex, and triple eyepiece.

This device accommodates two or more eyepieces in one mounting, so that you can change eyepieces by simply turning the unit. The fuss of removing, inserting, and focusing eyepieces again and again is avoided.

With some telescopes, a multiple eyepiece would hold the individual eyepieces too far from the objective. Before buying the device, determine whether it can be used without any modification of your telescope.

A simple clock drive: Used on equatorial telescope, this device keeps telescope sighted on celestial object despite Earth's rotation.

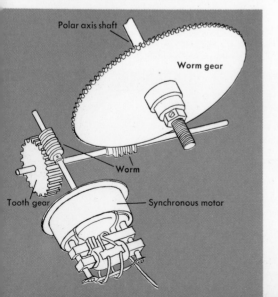

Polar axis shaft

Worm gear

Worm

Tooth gear

Synchronous motor

Special Eyepieces

Many eyepieces have been designed for specific purposes. Most are offered under the names of their inventors, such as Kellner, Ramsden, and Abbé.

The Kellner is recommended for wide fields with accurate color and images good to the edges. The Ramsden is favored by many for planetary observing.

The Abbé orthoscopic eyepiece is favored by observers who must wear their glasses at the telescope. The image is formed farther out from the eyepiece. The Abbé gives a large, highly corrected, colorless field.

The Barlow lens, designed to be used with regular eyepieces, can be adjusted so as to increase the magnifying power of any eyepiece by as much as three times. Thus it gives flexibility to one's equipment. It reduces the field of view, and does not raise the limit of useful magnification as determined by the objective

(see page 16). Many observers, however, swear by it.

Color Filters

Color filters "stop" certain colors and allow others to come through. Certain details can be distinguished only if a color filter is used to increase the contrast between them.

Filters transmit the color of the filter; thus, a red filter transmits red, and other colors such as green or blue appear dark. Since filters absorb some of the light, they may be used to cut down glare, such as Moon glare or the glare of the sky when you are observing Venus in daylight. Red, green, and blue filters are contrast filters.

A solar eyepiece has a very dense glass filter fitted to the cap of the eyepiece. For planets, colored optical glass filters can be purchased from optical goods supply stores. Or you can make filters out of Wratten gelatin filter sheets.

How Barlow lens works: By changing angle at which light from objective strikes eyepiece, Barlow lens in effect increases focal length of objective and thus increases magnification.

What filters can do: Mars as seen without filter (above) and through red filter (below).

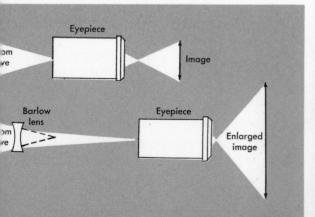

Gordon W. Smith

Backyard observatory: Eight-foot dome houses a 4-inch refractor. Dome can be rotated.

To make a filter, unscrew the cap of an eyepiece. Cut a piece of the gelatin sheet to fit it. Then screw the cover back on the eyepiece, just tight enough to hold firmly but not so tight as to wrinkle the filter.

Gelatin filters are perfectly safe with Moon, planets, and stars. *Do not* use them when looking at the Sun through a telescope (see page 50).

For the Moon, neutral filters cut down glare. Polarizing filters, or Polaroid, reduce intensity of background light when you are observing in daylight.

Another backyard observatory: Many amateurs have built this type. Roof slides back.

R. Newton Mayall

For planets, use red, green, and blue filters. For Jupiter and Venus in daytime, use Wratten K2, or Polaroid to reduce sky intensity.

A Second Telescope

Some sky observers treat themselves to an "extra" telescope. The owner of a long-focus instrument, used for planet study, gets himself a short-focus "rich-field" for viewing broad star fields. Another observer's 8-inch reflector is too big to take on vacations; so he acquires a 50mm. refractor. The would-be satellite tracker or meteor watcher whose general-purpose 6-inch reflector provides a field of 2° or less brings home a wide-field portable tracking scope. Possession of two telescopes, especially if they are of widely differing types, means plenty of opportunities for interesting experiments as well as variety in observing.

The Observatory

Many amateurs have made their own observatories, with peaked or flat roofs that can be removed, opened, or slid out of the way. Some even have domes. An observatory saves time and energy that ordinarily go into carrying an instrument around and setting it up. A shelter gives protection from the wind, and makes a convenient place for storing books, maps, and equipment.

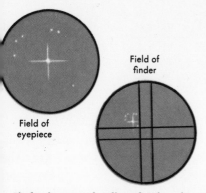

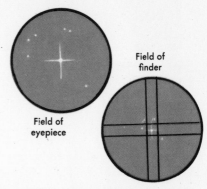

Finder improperly aligned: When object is centered in eyepiece, it is not centered in finder.

Finder properly aligned: When object is centered in eyepiece, it is also centered in finder.

CARE OF EQUIPMENT

All equipment should be inspected frequently. Reflectors require more care and maintenance than refractors.

Reflecting telescopes require frequent checking of the collimation (alignment) of the diagonal mirror or prism with the objective and eyepiece. Improper alignment will cause blurred, fuzzy, or distorted images.

The finder should be checked often. Improper adjustment makes it hard to sight the telescope when high powers are used and the field of view is, therefore, small.

There should be no "play" in the telescope mounting. When moved to a position, the tube should stay there without "springing," if the counterweight is properly adjusted.

If the optical surfaces are good, and everything is aligned, and the seeing is favorable, the brighter stars will appear as neat dots of light.

Around these dots you may be able to see one or two very faint concentric rings of light, called diffraction rings. These are normal in an instrument of good quality.

Alignment is poor if the objective or mirror is not set exactly at right angles to the tube; if the eyepiece is out of line; or—in the case of reflectors—if the secondary mirror needs adjustment. Scratches on the surfaces of the objective or eyepiece also can blur images.

Alignment of optical system: Good instrument, properly aligned, shows stars and planets as neat points or disks (left). Poor alignment causes ragged or distorted images (right).

Good alignment

Poor alignment

Storage

If a telescope is taken from a warm house out into the cold, it may perform poorly for 15 minutes or more —until it becomes adjusted to the temperature change. The same is true if the instrument is taken from a cold place to a warm one. Some observers arrange a safe place for their telescope in an unheated garage or barn, where outdoor temperatures prevail.

Before observing, set the telescope in the open air for a while. Don't try to observe from a warm room with the telescope pointed out the window. Warm air currents around the instrument will distort the images.

After the evening's observing, cover the telescope properly. The open end of the tube of a reflector should be covered with a bag or cap for protection against dust. (Protectors can be made with cardboard, chamois, or plastic.) A refractor should be similarly protected. Some reflectors are open at the mirror end, which should be covered, or a cap can be placed over the mirror itself.

If you take a telescope from cold air into a warm room, don't cover it until any dew that has formed on the lens or mirror has disappeared. Otherwise spotting of the optical surfaces may occur.

Do not try to remove moisture from the object glass or mirror with a cloth. Wait until all the moisture has evaporated; then remove any dust with a camel's-hair brush.

Remove the eyepiece before storing the telescope. Keep your eyepieces in a separate, padded, dustproof box.

Jolting and jarring tend to get optical parts out of line and, occasionally, may result in serious damage. This hazard applies to reflectors especially. Your telescope will appreciate minimum handling.

Alignment of primary mirror in Newtonian reflector: If mirror is properly aligned, diagonal and its reflection appear centered when seen from open end of tube.

Distance of diagonal from primary mirror in reflector: If distance is correct, reflection of diagonal will be centered when viewed through eyepiece holder opening with eye close to holder.

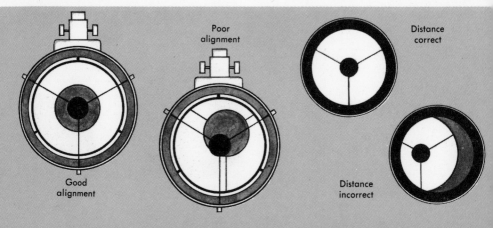

Poor alignment

Distance correct

Good alignment

Distance incorrect

Correcting Poor Alignment

Misalignment is the most common ailment of reflectors. Well-made reflectors have adjustable parts so that alignment can be readily corrected.

In the Newtonian reflector (the most common type), take measurements to see that the diagonal mirror or prism is centered in the tube. Next (with adequate lighting), look into the tube from the open end. The diagonal should be centered against its enlarged reflection in the mirror; if not, the mirror needs adjustment.

Finally, look through the empty eyepiece holder at the diagonal. The reflections from the diagonal should be on center as you look directly down the center of the eyepiece holder; if not, the diagonal needs attention. Try various adjustments.

Cleaning Optical Surfaces

The proper cleaning of lenses and mirrors is a delicate process. It should be done only by trained persons or by those who follow proper procedure carefully. A tiny piece of grit on a piece of cloth or paper that you use for wiping the lens or mirror may leave scratches that permanently impair performance. Never *rub* a lens or mirror; never touch the optical surface with your fingers.

So far as practicable, remove dirt by dusting with a camel's-hair brush. If further cleaning is needed, the lens or

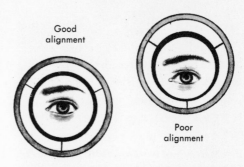

Good alignment

Poor alignment

Alignment of diagonal in reflector: If diagonal is properly aligned, reflection of eye and mirror will be centered when viewed through eyepiece holder with eye far out from holder.

mirror can be dabbed (*not* rubbed!) gently with a mild soap-and-water solution, then rinsed thoroughly in clear water and allowed to dry in the air.

Eyepieces, too, require careful handling. They should not be immersed. Full instructions on the cleaning of eyepieces, as well as objectives, are given in books on telescope making (page 113). Eyepieces are very precisely assembled, and should not be taken apart except by a person who knows how.

Lightly dust optical parts frequently. Beyond that, frequent cleaning can be as bad as none at all. Lenses and mirrors that are subjected to no more than the normal dust, dewing,

Eyepiece storage: Eyepieces, as well as filters and other small accessories, should be kept in a convenient dust-tight box.

Two portable telescopes: Short-focus 5-inch refractor (left), easily carried, is handy for viewing Moon, clusters, and other objects not requiring high magnification. Six-inch reflector (right), with longer focal length, makes good general-purpose instrument.

and chemical action of the atmosphere may need cleaning only once a year. Remember: slight soiling is not so bad as scratched glass or a badly worn mirror coating due to excessive zeal about cleaning.

Telescope on wheels: Homemade 8-inch reflector, too heavy to carry about, is kept in garage and wheeled out at observing time.

Other Maintenance

Eventually the mirror of a reflector will need recoating. Silver coatings may last as little as six months. Aluminum coatings are harder, are more easily cleaned, and may do for many years. The coating of mirrors is a job strictly for professionals.

When your telescope is in use, be sure that all parts move easily. If any part works hard, never try to force it. Find out what is wrong before using it any further. Hint: check clamps in right ascension and declination.

Some moving parts may require lubrication. This should be done with the frequency and kind of lubricant recommended by the manufacturer.

Most refractors come equipped with a dew cap that fits tightly over the objective. Use it while observing. It helps to keep dew from forming on the lens. If a dew cap is not a part of your equipment, you can make one out of a cardboard tube. Paint the inside black—a flat black, not enamel or any other glossy finish. Make sure of a tight fit, and let the tube extend beyond the objective about 6 to 9 inches.

If you want to make your own reflecting telescope, check reliable magazines or books (page 113) for suitable designs.

Proper care and maintenance will add to the life of your equipment and vastly increase the pleasure you get out of it.

INCIDENTAL INFORMATION

Some Amateur Observing Groups

American Association of Variable Star Observers (AAVSO), 4 Brattle St., Cambridge 38, Mass. World-wide; largest group of amateurs doing serious work. Members' observations of variable stars are processed and made available to astronomers throughout world. Other divisions: sunspots, auroras, occultations.

American Meteor Society (AMS), 521 N. Wynnewood Avenue, Narberth, Pa. Stresses visual and telescopic observations of meteors.

Association of Lunar and Planetary Observers (ALPO), 1835 Evans Place, Las Cruces, N.M. Informal, international group studies Moon, planets, etc. Section Recorders supervise systematic work.

Royal Astronomical Society of New Zealand (RASNZ), c/o Carter Observatory, P.O. Box 2909, Wellington C.1, N. Z. Sections do variable-star observing, telescope making, lunar and planetary observing, and computing.

For Reference

ANNUALS

American Ephemeris and Nautical Almanac (Superintendent of Documents, Washington 25, D.C.) : Up-to-date information about Sun, Moon, planets, occultations, and eclipses.

Observer's Handbook (Royal Astronomical Society of Canada, Toronto, Canada) : Handy guide to celestial events. Numerous tables.

STAR ATLASES

Atlas of the Heavens, by A. Becvar (Sky Publishing Corp., Cambridge, Mass.) : Charts of entire sky show stars to magnitude 7.75, with clusters, nebulas, double stars, and variables.

Norton's Star Atlas and Telescopic Handbook, by Arthur P. Norton (Sky Publishing Corp., Cambridge, Mass.) : Maps of entire sky show stars to magnitude 6, with clusters, nebulas, galaxies, and variables. Many pages of valuable information.

Webb's Atlas of the Stars (Harold B. Webb, Lynbrook, N.Y.) : Charts show stars to magnitude 9, from North Pole to −23°. Highly useful with telescope. Locates most long-period variables observed by AAVSO.

MAGAZINES

Sky and Telescope (Sky Publishing Corp., Cambridge, Mass.; monthly) : Foremost popular magazine on astronomy. News; authoritative, illustrated articles and departments. Advertisements of books on astronomy, maps and slides, telescopes and accessories.

The Strolling Astronomer (Walter Haas, 1835 Evans Place, Las Cruces, N. M.) : The journal of the Association of Lunar and Planetary Observers. Articles on planets, Moon, etc., with many drawings and photos.

GENERAL INFORMATION

Amateur Telescope Making, compiled by Albert G. Ingalls. (Scientific American, Inc., 415 Madison Ave., New York) : Rich in practical information about telescopes. 3 vols.

Astronomy, by Robert H. Baker (D. Van Nostrand Co., Princeton, N. J.) : Standard text.

Celestial Objects for Common Telescopes, Vol. II, by Rev. T. W. Webb (Dover Publications, 920 Broadway, New York) : Describes nearly 4,000 interesting objects.

Field Book of the Skies, by Olcott and Mayall (G. P. Putnam's Sons, New York) : Standard guide. Includes star lore, charts for eye and binoculars, charts for telescope, tables.

Golden Book of Astronomy, by Rose Wyler and Gerald Ames (Golden Press, New York) : A children's classic. Colorful pictures.

Making Your Own Telescope, by Allyn J. Thompson (Sky Publishing Corp., Cambridge, Mass.) : Directions for 6-inch reflector.

New Handbook of the Heavens, by Bernhard, Bennett, and Rice (McGraw-Hill Book Co., New York) : Readable popular introduction to astronomy. (Also in paper-cover edition.)

Skyshooting, by R. N. and M. W. Mayall (Ronald Press Co., 15 East 26 St., New York) : Layman's guide to photography of heavens.

Stars, by H. S. Zim and R. H. Baker (Golden Press, New York) : Pocket guide with much practical information. Richly illustrated.

Stars of the Southern Heavens, by James Nangle (Angus and Robertson, Sydney, Australia) : For observers in southern latitudes.

Telescopes and Their Accessories, by G. Z. Dimitroff and J. G. Baker (Harvard Univ. Press, Cambridge, Mass.) : A reference text.

MAPS OF THE HEAVENS

The charts on this and the following pages have been prepared expressly for use with this book. The accuracy of the charts is consistent with their size and the multicolor printing process used. About 1,500 stars, down to 5th magnitude, are plotted for Epoch 1900. All the variables, double stars, novas, galaxies, and nebulas listed elsewhere in the book are located. Symbols are explained in keys beneath the charts.

Where two stars are too close to show separately, a single disk represents the brighter one. Both may be designated, e.g. $\phi^{1,2}$; or only one may be designated, e.g. ϕ^2.

Some of the customary constellation outlines have been altered. Connecting lines between stars are drawn more to help the observer "get around" than to represent mythological figures.

Five colors are used to show the spectral classes of stars. In each spectral class a certain color is predominant, and it is this color that appears on the chart.

The charts are in five parts: three for the equatorial region, from $+46°$ to $-46°$, and two for the polar regions, from $+90°$ to $+44°$ and from $-90°$ to $-44°$.

Along the top of each equatorial chart appear indications of right

(Continued on page 122)

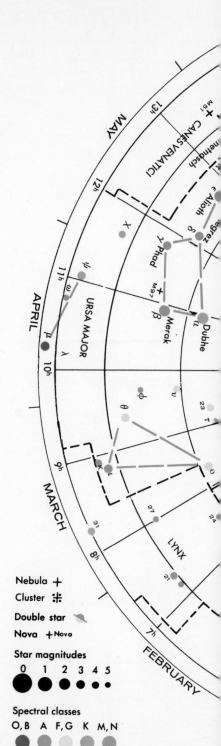

Nebula +
Cluster ✳
Double star ◥
Nova +Nova

Star magnitudes
0 1 2 3 4 5

Spectral classes
O,B A F,G K M,N

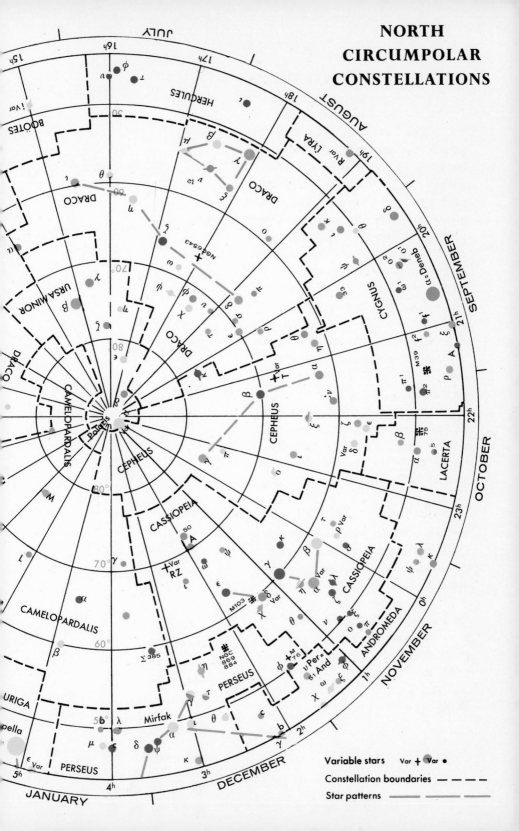

NORTH CIRCUMPOLAR CONSTELLATIONS

Variable stars   Var ✛ Var ●
Constellation boundaries — — —
Star patterns ▬▬▬ ▬▬▬

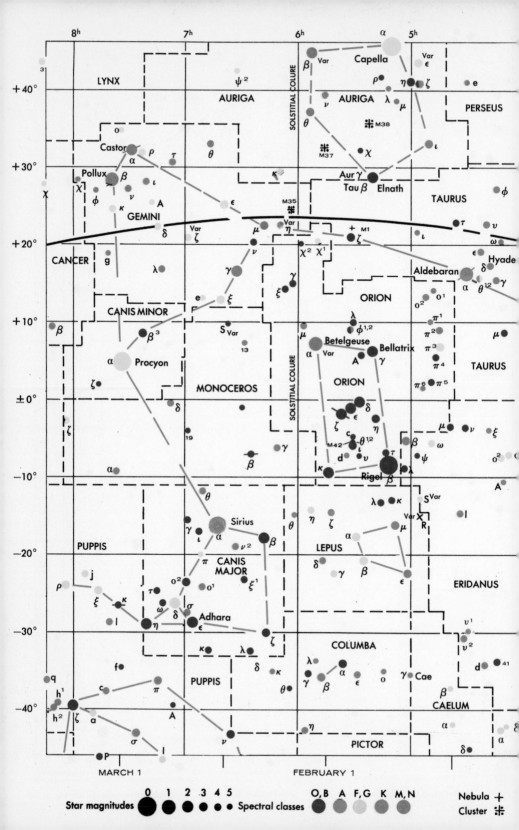

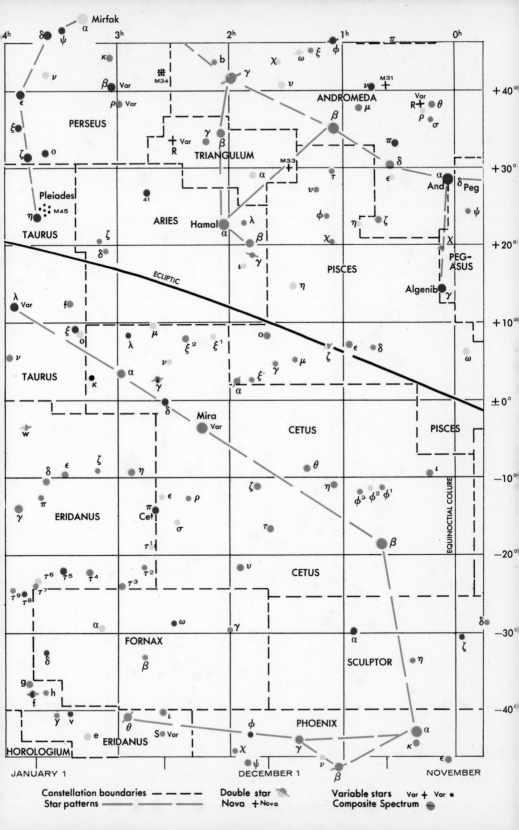

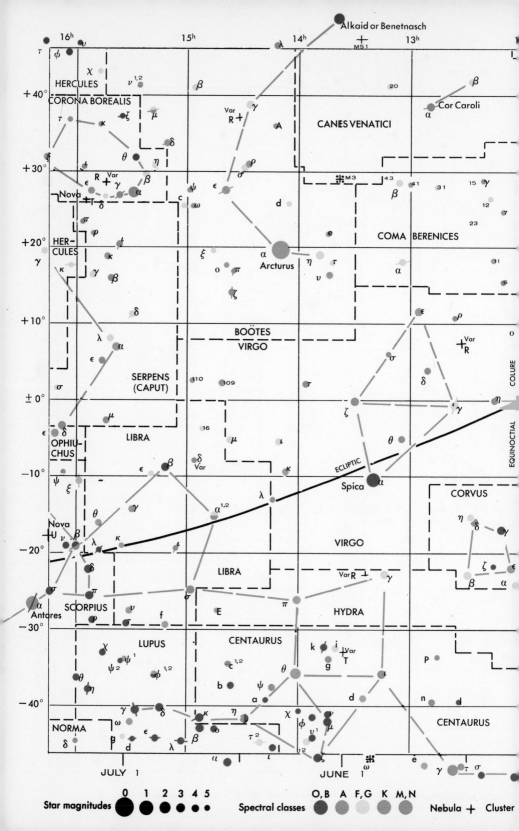

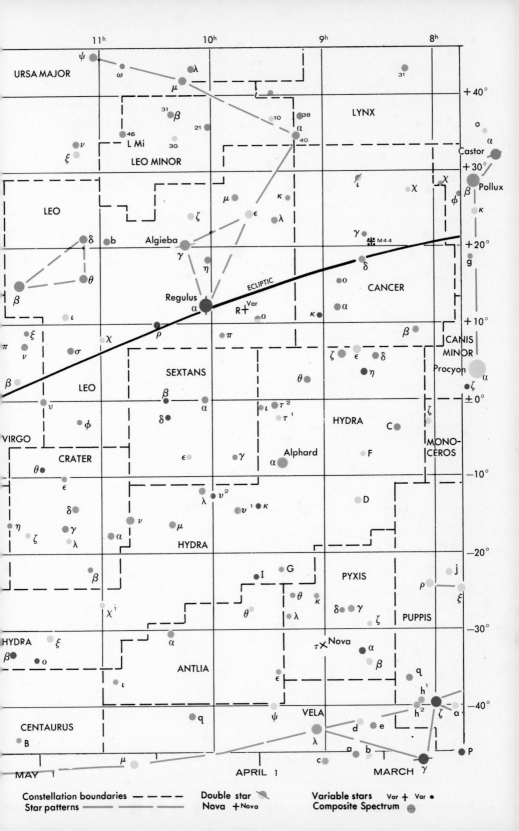

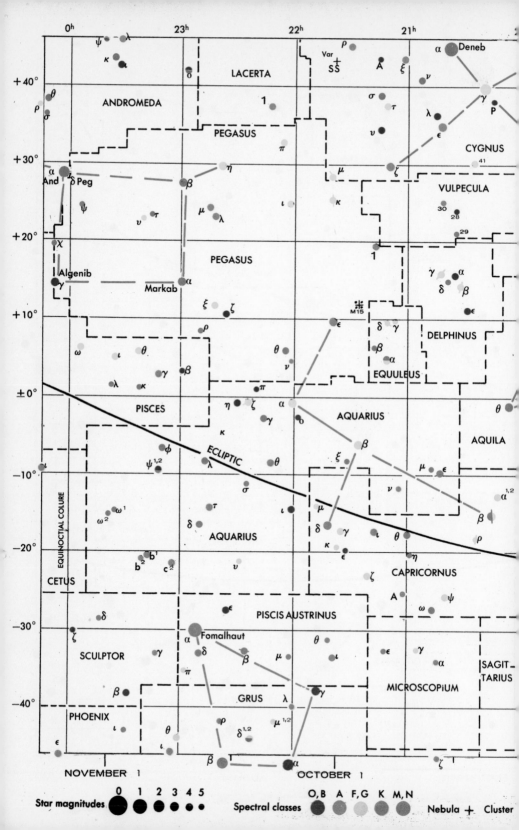

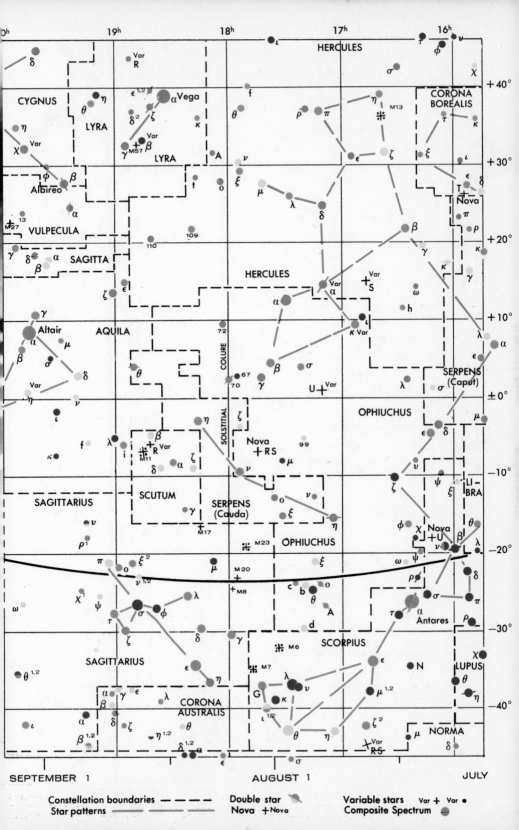

(Continued from page 114)

ascension, and at each side, declination. On the polar charts, right ascension is marked around the edge, and declination where convenient.

Dates along the bottom of each equatorial chart show the time of year when each constellation is most conveniently placed for viewing; that is, when it reaches its highest point above the horizon (the meridian) at 9 p.m. A star arrives at the meridian 4 minutes earlier each night.

Equatorial charts are used when you are facing away from the pole; polar charts, when facing the poles.

Only observers at the equator can see all parts of the heavens shown by these charts. Observers in the northern hemisphere cannot see some part of the southern skies, and to observers in the southern hemisphere some part of the northern skies is invisible.

An observer at +40° latitude theoretically has a southern horizon that cuts the celestial sphere at −50° declination. But seldom can we satisfactorily observe any object within 10° of the horizon. Therefore the useful observing horizon at +40° latitude would be at about −40° declination. For a southern observer at −40° latitude, the useful northern horizon would be at +40°.

Draw a horizontal line on each equatorial chart to show your useful observing horizon. Then you can always tell at a glance which objects are too far south or north for you.

Nebula +

Cluster ❊

Double star ❧

Nova +Nova

Star magnitudes

0 1 2 3 4 5

Spectral classes

O,B   A   F,G   K   M,N

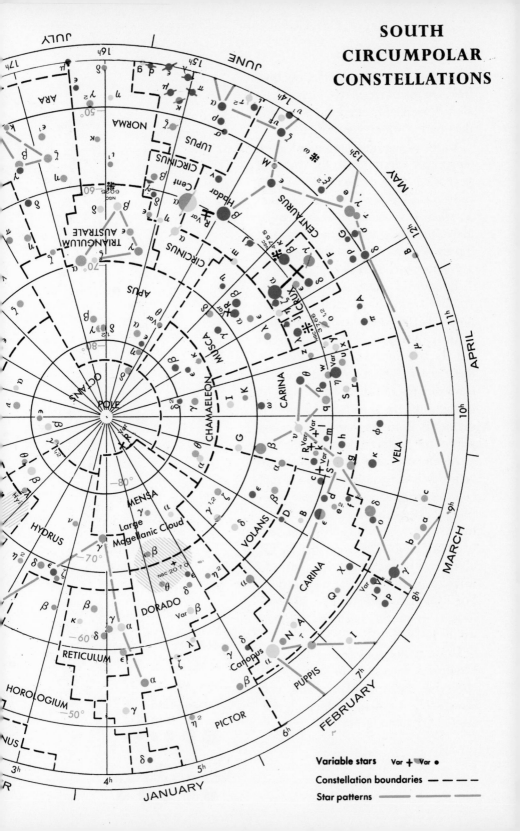

SOUTH
CIRCUMPOLAR
CONSTELLATIONS

Variable stars   Var + Var •

Constellation boundaries - - - - -

Star patterns

INDEX

Listed in this index are the 88 constellations shown on the star maps (pages 114-123), with their common names. Page numbers in **boldface** indicate pages where subjects are illustrated.

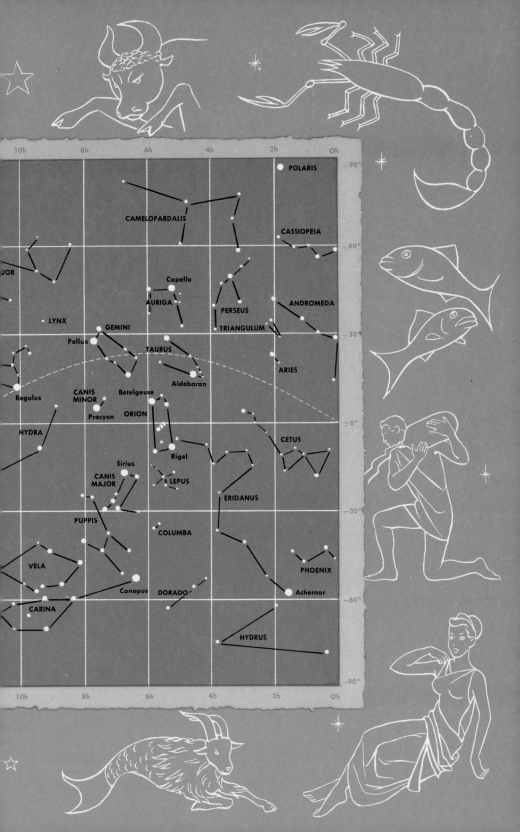

CAMELOPARDALIS

POLARIS

CASSIOPEIA

+90°

+60°

ANDROMEDA

Capella

AURIGA

PERSEUS

TRIANGULUM

+30°

LYNX

GEMINI

Pollux

TAURUS

ARIES

Regulus

CANIS MINOR

Betelgeuse

Aldebaran

±0°

Procyon

ORION

CETUS

HYDRA

Rigel

Sirius

CANIS MAJOR

LEPUS

−30°

PUPPIS

ERIDANUS

COLUMBA

VELA

PHOENIX

Canopus

DORADO

Achernar

−60°

CARINA

HYDRUS

−90°

10h   8h   6h   4h   2h   0h

10h   8h   6h   4h   2h   0h

JOR